CHINESE FOLK AND FAIRY TALES

In this collection of folk and fairy tales from China, a land where wonders have never ceased, there are tales of romance and adventure, of luck, of marvelous happenings, and of strange and almost lovable beasts such as the Nung-guama and the Wang Liang (perhaps the original Abominable Snowman).

Here for people of all ages are stories which can be read aloud, folk and fairy tales of the Old World of Ancient China.

Other books in the same series:

RUSSIAN FOLK AND FAIRY TALES, E. M. Almedingen
FRENCH FOLK AND FAIRY TALES, Roland Gant
GERMAN FOLK AND FAIRY TALES,
    Maurice and Pamela Michael
ENGLISH FAIRY TALES, Joseph Jacobs
MORE ENGLISH FAiRY TALES, Joseph Jacobs
CELTIC FAIRY TALES, Joseph Jacobs
INDIAN FAIRY TALES, Joseph Jacobs

All handsomely illustrated

CHINESE
FOLK AND FAIRY TALES

Leslie Bonnet

illustrated by Maurice Brevannes

FOLK AND FAIRY TALES FROM MANY LANDS

G. P. PUTNAM'S SONS
NEW YORK

ACKNOWLEDGMENT

The stories which I have related here come from three sources. I want to acknowledge my indebtedness to Wolfram Eberhard for his scholarly *Chinese Fairy Tales and Folk Tales*; to Chi-Chen Wang for his felicitous translations, *Traditional Chinese Tales;* and to my dear friends of the Peiping Players in Chengtu, from whom I first learned so many of them.

Leslie Bonnet

CONTENTS

CONTENTS

The Man Who Loved Flowers

I T must have been twelve hundred years ago that Tsui Hsuan-wei lived in the Middle Kingdom.

He was one who sought to make himself perfect, and the way he chose to do this was a good way. He built a small house, and around it laid out a beautiful garden. And in this modest house, within his garden wall, Hsuan-wei lived alone in peace and contentment, enjoying the benefit of good thoughts.

The garden was gay with flowers, and this good man loved nothing more than to walk among them, tending them and admiring their fresh beauty.

One night a round, honey-colored moon hung in the sky, and the air was soft and still. As Hsuan-wei walked slowly among the fragrance of his flowers, he saw a maiden coming shyly toward him in the moonlight.

Hsuan-wei was surprised, almost alarmed, at this sight. It was many years since any person had come unbidden into his garden. While he watched, the maiden came nearer to him and finally stood meekly in front of him, her head downcast, her dark eyelashes fluttering with excitement.

Her behavior was very correct, and Hsuan-wei was a little reassured, so when she had bowed respectfully before him, he kindly asked her who she might be, and what she was doing there at this hour.

The maiden lifted a face of bright loveliness. "I live close by," she said. "My friends and I come this way tonight to visit our Aunt Feng. We beg that we may rest for awhile in your garden."

Hsuan-wei gladly agreed to this suggestion, and at once the

9

maiden's companions appeared; they must have been very close by all this time. They were a laughing, graceful group of young ladies, each dressed in a different color.

As they bowed, they gaily introduced themselves.

"I am Willow," said a girl in green.

"I am Plum," said one all in white.

"And I Chrysanthemum," laughed a plump little one in purple.

This went on for quite a time, for there must have been twenty or thirty maidens. The last to announce herself was one dressed in red. Her name was Pomegranate.

This young woman seemed to have more confidence than the rest. "We had hoped to see our Auntie Feng tonight," she told Hsuan-wei, "but she did not come. We therefore thought that we would go to visit her, and then it seemed that it would be delightful to stop and pay you some few compliments, because you have always been kind to us."

While they were yet talking, Auntie Feng appeared. She was a thin-featured woman with a chilling glance. Hsuan-wei felt quite cold at the sight of her.

When this lady had been presented to him by the chattering maidens, Hsuan-wei made instant preparations for a small feast, and in quite a short time they were all seated in his house and enjoying fine foods and rare wines. The moon shone more and more brightly, and the room was so filled with fragrance that it seemed almost as if all the flowers in the garden had crowded inside.

Pomegranate filled a large cup of wine and presented it to Auntie Feng, the chief guest. Then, glowing in her red robe, she sang a song. It was about the sad shortness of youth, and of how it was useless to blame the wind for this, when it was something which just had to happen.

The song was very well received by the maidens and by their host, who exclaimed, "Good! Good!" in a warm voice. But Auntie Feng did not show any pleasure.

Then Plum, very white in the moon's radiance, sang a song. And this, too, was about how one was young and fresh for such a little time, and how useless it was to reproach the harsh wind for this.

While this song was being sung, Auntie Feng, who had not touched the cup of wine which Plum had first presented to her, began to look very cold indeed. And when Plum had finished and the maidens had all expressed their pleasure, Auntie Feng spoke.

"I cannot think," she said frigidly, "why you should choose to sing such dismal songs in a gathering so agreeable as this. Please do not imagine that I have not noticed the criticism of myself in the words you have sung. Now, as a punishment, you, Pomegranate, and you, Plum, must each drink a large cup of wine; and then sing a song about cheerful matters." And, saying this, Auntie Feng filled two cups with wine and handed them to the abashed girls.

It was very unfortunate that one cup should be spilled, and even more unfortunate that it should be spilled over the red dress of Pomegranate. For Pomegranate was not only very careful of her gowns, but she was also (alas!) a little high spirited.

Instead of accepting the rebuke of an elder person with cheerfulness, she quite lost her temper.

"The others may be afraid of you," she said impertinently to Auntie Feng, "but I am not." And with that she stalked out of the room with as much firmness as a young person so soft and frail can manage.

Auntie Feng was very angry. She got up from the table. "Who is this impertinent young girl," she demanded, "who dares to speak to me in such a fashion?"

The other girls tried at once to pacify her. "She is but young and ignorant. She will repent and ask your pardon in the morning."

Hsuan-wei, too, did all that he could to restore good humor to Auntie Feng, but no one could calm her anger. Still cold with rage, she went away. And when Auntie Feng departed, so did all the pretty maidens. At one moment the room was a jostle of excited girls; the next moment it was empty. The moon had slipped down, and the warm scent of flowers was gone.

The host, hoping at least to part with his guests in a seemly manner, ran out into the garden to catch them and give them parting greetings, but in the darkness he tripped over a stone, and by the time he had got to his feet again the voices of his visitors had faded away.

However, the next evening Hsuan-wei was in his garden as soon as it was dusk. He was very pleased to find that the maidens were already there. They stood in a glimmering group, scolding Pomegranate and trying to persuade her to apologize to Auntie Feng.

When Pomegranate saw Hsuan-wei approach, she broke away from the group of girls and ran lightly to him. Then, placing herself a little behind him, she said to the others, from around his elbow. "Why should we trouble ourselves to apologize to Auntie Feng, when our good friend here can protect us?"

This suggestion seemed to please her friends. At once they gave up chiding Pomegranate, and laughing and chattering, ran up to their host and looked up at him expectantly.

A little alarmed at this situation, Hsuan-wei asked hopelessly: "But in what way can I protect you?"

"Oh! It is a very simple matter," Pomegranate assured him. "You have only to make a banner; and on the banner must be painted the sun and the moon and the four constellations. On the first morning when there is a wind from the east you must set up this banner in the eastern part of your garden. In this way you will protect us."

Hsuan-wei willingly promised to do this, and no sooner had he promised than the maidens vanished. When he stared about him, all he could see were tree blossoms and garden flowers, nodding to him as if they were friends.

That very day Hsuan-wei made the banner, and on the first morning when a light breeze from the east stirred the flowers he set it up firmly in the eastern part of the garden.

The light breeze freshened and then began to blow until the tall trees outside the garden seemed to clap their hands and rock upon their feet. It blew until roofs rattled and branches snapped. In the countryside whole forests were uprooted, and river waters were blown upstream. But inside Hsuan-wei's garden, where the magic banner hung listless, not a breath of wind disturbed the trees and flowers.

Now Hsuan-wei could clearly see that Auntie Feng was none other than the east wind, and that the little ladies were in truth flowers themselves. But this did not lead him to treat their advice lightly when in the evening, after the storm was passed, they came running to thank him.

They were all there in their bright colors. Each brought him a handful of flower petals.

"To eat," each one said prettily as she pressed the petals into his hands.

"To eat," said Pomegranate, coming last of all in her red gown. "To eat." Her voice was as clear as trickling water. "It will keep off old age."

And when Hsuan-wei did faithfully eat all those petals, it must be said that he at once began to look like a young man. And with the time he thus gained, and because of his virtuous life, he did at last become an Immortal.

The Girl on the Green Tree

I N old China the wife had to obey, not only the husband, but the mother-in-law; it was mother-in-law who ruled the house.

To the Shao family, who lived to the north of the Yi-lu mountain, there came to live a young woman who was to be married to the second son.

She was made to work bitterly hard.

There was a peculiar tree growing in the garden of the Shao family. Its leaves remained green all the year through. And every morning round pieces of copper fell from it. If holes were knocked through the middle of these, they looked exactly like money, and of course the Shao family used them for money.

But making a round hole in the middle of each piece of copper was hard and difficult. The hammer soon blistered the hands. The poor daughter-in-law-to-be was made to do this. The difficulty was that the time spent on this might interfere with the rest of her day's work, but this problem was solved by sending her out into the garden before it was light. In this way she finished punching her holes by the time the sun rose, and could then start her day's work by going up onto the mountain to collect wood. If collecting wood with blistered hands was painful, that was a matter that concerned no one but the girl herself. It was fortunate for all that she was there and able to do these disagreeable tasks.

It was cold, too, up on the mountain, and the frail girl had no more than a couple of rags to cover her. How she used to shiver on winter mornings! The Shaos, still snug indoors, often said, "It must be cold for her up there."

15

You must not think that she bore all this with patient resignation. She often used to weep as well as shiver. The mountainside was a convenient place for weeping, because the mother-in-law-to-be was impatient of people who wept in her hearing.

One morning on the mountain, her bones creaking with the cold, the girl sat on a boulder and wept and lamented her hard lot. After awhile an ancient man came hobbling out of a grove of pine trees and asked her why she cried so bitterly.

Nobody had spoken kindly to the girl for a long time, and so she told this old man all the story. She told him of the peculiar green tree, and how it dropped round pieces of copper every morning, and how she had to hammer a hole in each piece.

The old man listened in silence, nodding in the saddest parts of the story.

When she had finished, he pointed with his staff toward the mountain top. "Do you see that stone man up there?" he asked.

The girl looked. There did seem to be a piece of rock which was shaped like a man.

"He points his hand, does he not?" asked the ancient person.

"Yes." The girl could see what looked like an outstretched arm, pointing.

"Ah!" said the old one. "He points his finger at the strange tree in the Shao's garden. That is what makes it shed copper coins. If that finger were broken off, the tree would die."

This piece of news seemed to the girl to take some of the keenness out of the morning wind. She thanked the old man, and then, picking up her small gathering of kindling, she wandered off, with a better heart, to search for more.

The next morning, when she went shivering up the mountain, she carried the hammer, hidden under her arm. Straight up she went to the mountain's top, and with one angry blow knocked the finger from the stone man.

And sure enough, though she searched about with numbed hands in the half-light of the following morning, there was not a copper piece to be found under the tree in the Shao's garden. When at last the red sun looked over the side of the Yi-lu mountain and shed rosy light down into the garden, the girl could see that the tree was withered and dead.

When the mother-in-law-to-be discovered this, she was furious. That was to be expected. All that free money was now gone. The old woman guessed at once that in some way the girl had brought this about. It had been difficult for the maiden to show a proper degree of sorrow at the death of a tree which had meant so much cruel work for her.

The old lady screamed with rage. "All right! If you will kill our tree, I will kill you!" and, with agility surprising for her age, she leapt for the chopper which had been left leaning against the wall.

The poor young girl did not wait for more. With a loud cry of alarm, she ran straight out of the garden and bounded away up the mountainside. She ran without stopping, and after her, brandishing the large chopper, scampered her mother-in-law-to-be. Happily the maiden was light and fleet and the old lady's legs were not so strong as they had once been. Moreover, the chopper was heavy. So the maiden was relieved to hear the angry cries of her pursuer grow gradually fainter with distance until she could hear them no more. Then, panting hard with her exertions, she stopped and looked back. The mother-in-law-to-be could be seen, away down there, sitting heavily upon a rock and sharpening the chopper upon it. The girl dared not go back.

But in that wild season there was no proper food to be found up on the mountain. The little bride-to-be wandered day after day, frozen and famished, amid that waste of rocks. All she could find to chew were the needles of the pine trees, and on this quite unpalatable fare she somehow managed to exist.

Then a really queer thing happened. After she had been living on these pine needles for a few months, she noticed that white hairs were growing all over her body. This alarmed her, although she took some comfort from the fact that the hairs did at least help to keep her warm. But they grew longer and longer, and then one evening she found that she could fly. The ground was hard with frost. The stars, as she circled the pointed tops of the pine trees, sparkled and twinkled like lamps at a festival. It was a delightful sensation to be hovering thus, high up in the crisp air. The maiden thought she would fly a short distance away and see what was to be found elsewhere.

Now, not far away, just outside the gate of the Chung-en temple, there was a magical pine tree. You could cut off any of the branches as often as you wished and they would grow again immediately.

One of the monks of the temple took special care of this remarkable tree, and not a morning passed when he did not walk out to inspect it, to make quite sure that it was in good condition. But on several mornings he noticed that the pine needles had been eaten off. He could not imagine what creature could be gnawing at them. He determined to find out.

One evening he hid and watched. Night came. A huge, honey-coloured moon floated over the fields and forests. Nothing stirred; only down in the village a dog howled. Then the monk heard a whistling noise up in the sky. He held his breath and watched. With a soft, swooping sound, a white creature came down out of the air onto the tree, and began to eat the pine needles. In the yellow moonlight its long hairs looked like sheep's wool.

The monk did not dare stir. He knew that this visitor must be either a ghost or one of the Immortals. The important thing was to find out which it was.

When the creature had eaten its fill and gone, the monk retired to sleep. In the morning he had an idea.

That evening, before he hid, he placed a sumptuous meal on a table under the tree. The enticing smell of it rose up into the topmost branches of the magic pine.

It was a clever trap that the monk had set. If the intruder were an Immortal, it would not touch the food; but if it were a ghost, it would be sure to gobble it up. In this way the monk would find out what kind of visitor he had to deal with.

When he hid himself, he took with him his magic sword, in case the creature turned out to be a ghost. If it were an Immortal, there would be nothing that the monk could do except to try excessively courteous persuasion.

Well, he waited, and eventually down came the white creature. But this time it did not stay in the branches of the pine tree any longer than was necessary to smell the delicious food below. Then, with one silent swoop, it was down on the table, cramming meat into its mouth with one hand and fish with the other.

Then the monk knew that it was a ghost. Waving his magic sword, he sprang out of hiding. "What kind of ghost are you?" he shouted boldly.

The frightened ghost tried hard to fly away, but because of the magic sword, this was impossible. And so it began to weep instead. The bold monk repeated his question.

The white ghost looked up from where it now knelt humbly before him, and said, "I am the daughter-in-law-to-be of the Shao family. I killed their magic tree. My mother-in-law-to-be chased me, that she might take my life from me. I fled to the mountain, and had to live on bitter pine needles. Then this long, white hair grew upon me and I began to fly. This pine tree has needles of a very sweet taste, and besides, they always grow again, so I hoped there would be no harm if I fed on them. I always came at night, Your Honor, so as not to create alarm. Then, when I smelt this beautiful food, I could not resist it. I do hope Your Honor will pardon my presumption."

The monk still maintained a stern look. Great care must be taken in dealing with ghosts, who will tell any lie that may happen to suit them.

"If you are in truth the daughter-in-law-to-be of the Shao family, you shall come to their house with me at once."

The poor ghost cried and trembled. "But my mother-in-law-to-be will kill me," she whimpered.

At this the monk was satisfied that the ghost was truly the young girl; he well knew the harsh disposition of the old lady Shao.

He spoke kindly now. "You shall sleep safely here at the monastery tonight," he said. "Tomorrow you shall return to the Shao house. But do not fear, I shall arrange everything." That night the girl slept warmly and in comfort for the first time for many months.

The next day the monk took her back to the Shao's house. It did not need his warnings to make mother Shao receive the girl without beating her. For the old lady had a very high respect for ghosts, and would not for the world do anything to offend one.

After eating proper human food for a few months, the girl's white hairs gradually dropped off and she was as beautiful as she had ever been. Indeed she seemed much more beautiful than before, because now her mother-in-law gave her fine clothes to wear, and did not expect her to do any more heavy work.

So when she was finally married to the second son Shao, the pretty bride could look forward to a life of happiness.

The Fairy Wife

Long, long ago there were four brothers.

The elder brother was to marry the Emperor's daughter. He would live in refinement and felicity. The second brother was to marry the daughter of a general, and could expect a life of great splendor. The third brother was engaged to the daughter of a minister, and would become a person of great consequence.

The fourth brother did not expect to marry at all. He was a quiet and thoughtful young man and must surely have been something of a poet, for he declared that he would marry no one but a fairy. His three brothers laughed loudly at this; but he did not take offense; he had expected that they would laugh.

All three brothers were to be married at the same time in the Emperor's palace. It would be hard to describe the magnificence of the preparations. On the day of the weddings the palace was thronged with people of the highest class. The guests colored robes, stiff with rich embroidery, were matched by the glorious and fantastic decorations. There was great feasting and rejoicing.

Amid all this, the fourth brother felt a little out of place. Without a wife, he looked on at the splendid scene with scanty enjoyment. After awhile, tiring of the noise and glitter, he went out of the palace, out of the city, away into the fields—to calm his spirits in a quiet walk.

The road led over a high-arched bridge. He leaned over the parapet, and looked down at the surging waters for a long time. When he began to resume his stroll, he came face to face with a young maiden of extraordinary beauty. She was of a

21

quite perfect shape, and the pale loveliness of her face would have made even the Lady of the Moon envious. There was no doubt in the fourth brother's mind, even for one moment, that this dazzling young woman was a fairy. Not one thought did he give to her humble clothes; without even a word of apology, he asked her to be his wife.

When she agreed to this proposal, the fourth brother went nearly mad with delight. His one thought was to have her borne, with proper respect, back to the palace to be made his wife. He did not stop to consider that, since she appeared to be as strong as a peasant girl, she could quite well walk back there with him. His mind leapt straight to the idea that she must be carried there in a litter, like any other lady of importance. So, begging her not to stir from the spot, he ran excitedly away, with great strides, toward the city. He ran so fast that his feet seemed not to touch the ground.

When he reached the palace he hurried wildly among the guests. "I've found a wife! I've found a wife!" he shouted, but all of them were enjoying themselves too much to attend to him.

At last he managed to find four servants to carry a litter, and with them he set off, full of impatience, to fetch his fairy girl.

She was still there at the bridge, waiting, and with all speed he had her carried back to the palace, just in time for them to be married with the other three couples. But you may be sure that many delicately arched eyebrows were raised in disdain of the humble bride of the fourth brother, in her rough country gown.

The day after the wedding, as is the custom, all four young wives visited their parents. Both the general and the minister were, of course, in attendance upon the Emperor at the palace, so it was to the palace that the wives of the first, second and third brothers went to present gifts. Because there did not seem to be any parents for the fourth brother's wife to visit, she, too, went to the palace with the rest.

The Emperor's daughter took Korean ginseng tea. The general's daughter took ginseng tea. The minister's daughter took quite choice tea, though it was neither ginseng nor Korean ginseng. The fourth brother's wife took just ordinary green tea. How she was looked down upon by the other three brides!

It was not long before the New Year came. And at that time all the sons went to pay respect to their parents-in-law, and to offer them presents. But the fourth brother remained sullenly at home.

"Why are you not going to the palace to offer congratulations?" his wife asked him.

"How can I go?" groaned the fourth brother unhappily. "I am poor, and I can provide no presents."

His lovely wife smiled a secret smile. "I will tell you how you may go," she said. Then without the least difficulty she made a horse of straw. The next thing she did was to unwind part of the bandage from one of her little bound feet. "Ride down to the seashore on this horse, dear husband," she urged him, "and lay this bandage upon the sea."

The fourth brother did as she told him. The horse cantered off with him; and when the seashore was reached, he cast the bandage upon the waves. Instantly a broad opening appeared in the sea, so that he could ride his straw horse along it. Where it led him, we can only guess, but when he came back he was smiling with happiness and bore with him a great burden of Korean ginseng tea. When that was divided up among the parents-in-law, there was no one after that who could despise the wife of the fourth brother.

It is on the fourteenth day of the first month that presents of special impressiveness must be offered. The wives of the three elder brothers twittered together like sparrows as they discussed what things each of them should buy. The fourth brother began to look downhearted when he heard of all these preparations. His wife said to him, "Husband, go down to the seashore. Fetch for me the box you will see drifting in the shallows."

The fourth brother went. And there, no doubt of it, was a wooden chest, bobbing about in the placid waves of a calm sea. Lifting up his gown, he waded out to it. What a disappointment! When he lifted it up, it was just a battered old thing of rotting wood. Very cross at this (for he had expected that his wife's intention was to provide some present as impressive as the Korean ginseng tea had been), the fourth brother dropped the useless box back into the water and made his way home.

When he got there his pretty wife met him. "Have you brought the box?" she asked, looking quite excited.

The fourth brother stared at her hard. "It was only a rotten old chest that I saw," he told her. "Of what use would that be? I threw it back into the sea."

The pale, shining lady put a hand to her brow in weariness, for of course, to a fairy wife, a human husband can sometimes seem very tiresome indeed. But she did not scold. Smiling brightly, she looked up at him as she placed her hands on his shoulders. "Go back, dear husband, and fetch me that same old wooden chest," she pleaded.

Back he went and fetched home the wooden chest. He gave it to his wife without asking any questions, though you may be sure that on his way home he had grumbled about its uselessness and groaned because of its weight.

But when, on the evening of the fourteenth day, the fairy wife opened the creaking lid of the old box, the fourth brother stepped back with a cry of wonder. There, inside the box and yet as large as life, big enough to walk into, was another world. There was a great city with long streets. There were noble houses, and theatres in which exciting plays were being performed. All the shops were full of strange, rich merchandise. There were large parks in the city where remarkable flowers bloomed in gay profusion and where rare animals were kept to be gazed upon. There were lions and tigers and dragons of many colors, all horned and fire-breathing. There were elephants, too. The fourth brother had never seen such creatures.

When they had come out again from this city and his wife had closed the lid of the box, the fourth brother was quite dazed.

Of course he invited his brothers and his sisters-in-law to come and see this marvelous thing. His wife opened the lid, and there again was the fair city, its streets bright with gaily clad people. The whole party went down into the city. What a memorable evening they had! They went to one of the theatres, and never had they seen a play so entrancing or one acted with such grace and skill. They dined at a restaurant, on sharks' fins, ducks' feet, chicken livers, rare fish, swallows' nests, sea slugs, water chestnuts, bamboo shoots, and eggs one hundred years old.

So exciting and enjoyable it was that they stayed eating and drinking and talking happily until it was almost dawn.

But do you think that the wives of the three elder brothers were grateful for this cheerful evening? They were not. Each one cherished a feeling of hatred towards the fourth brother's wife, because she had provided a present which was incomparably the best. When they told their fathers of this wonder, they did so in tones of spite and envy.

It is not surprising, then, that the three husbands greatly desired to see the magic box again. But the Emperor would not let his son-in-law go a second time; he thought he would go himself. The bold general and the grave minister were of the same opinion.

The Emperor said in his heart, This must be the most wonderful thing in the world. It is too good for any subject to possess. I must have it for myself.

The general said thoughtfully, This box would be most useful to me in war. Surely the king of this magic city must have an army which I could borrow to help me to win my battles?

The minister stroked his thin straggle of beard, and thought, In such a city there must be many rich citizens. Perhaps I could tax them on the Emperor's behalf. Then, no doubt, out of all the money I collected for him, quite a lot would stick to my own fingers.

In fact by the time the three of them came to visit the box, each one had decided how he would possess himself of it. The Emperor's plan was the simplest. To live in more splendor than the Emperor himself was naturally an offense punishable by death. By owning this curious box, the fourth brother and his wife were outrivaling the Emperor, so that they deserved to be beheaded with a sword.

The general had decided that he would use his army to attack and destroy this couple.

The minister felt sure that he would only have to whisper some false story about them at the court, so that he could then have them banished to some place so far away that they could never get back from it.

They all went down into the box city together—the Emperor, the general, the minister, and the fourth brother and his wife. Because the Emperor was one of the party, they had to go to the palace in this city. Strangely, there was no king there to welcome them, but servants and soldiers there were in plenty. The Emperor, seating himself in the great hall, called loudly for wine.

This was brought very promptly, and the Emperor began to drink. The others stood by, attentive and respectful. They could not seat themselves or drink the wine unless the Emperor ordered them to do so. It did not occur to him to do this.

As the Emperor drank, his brow began to crease with thoughts. Between sips, his mouth shut hard. His eyes grew narrow. He looked quickly this way and then that way. Without doubt, he was thinking, this cowardly general and this dishonest minister both plot to obtain the wonderful box. If they succeed, what will they do? Destroy me? His long fingers twitched. His face darkened with rage.

Suddenly his suspicious anger blazed. He called loudly for the captain of the soldiers. Almost before one could think, both the general and the minister were killed. There were left only the fourth brother, breathing very quickly; his young wife, who hid her face on his shoulder; and the Emperor, who drank wine and looked up at them both mistrustfully, from moment to moment.

Then the water came in, flowing swiftly in a smooth trickle across the green stone floor of the vast hall, welling up deeper until it touched the ankles of the fourth brother and his fairy wife.

The Emperor did not seem to notice it at all. The little wife tugged urgently at the fourth brother's arm, and drew him away. They went quickly out of the hall, their feet making loud splashings. The Emperor did not move or speak. They went out of the palace into the flooded street where the waters swirled knee high. Before they got out of the box the water was up to their waists. It was a great relief to them to get back safely into the dry comfort of their own home.

The fairy wife shut the lid of the old box firmly. "Put it outside, dear husband," she said. "See, it is all wet."

Nobody ever saw the Emperor again. He sat there, drinking wine, till the water reached his waist, his chest, his shoulders. Soon his beard was floating like seaweed. Still he drank wine and frowned. Soon there was only the frown on his face to be seen; and that was the end of him.

The Three Copper Pieces

THERE was once a man who peddled tobacco. All day long he would trudge the city streets, with a pole over his shoulder, from which hung two wicker trays holding the tobacco.

It was a hard trade. He had to push his way down the Street of Embroiderers, through the thronging people, and then, turning into the Street of Silversmiths, make his way as far as the West Gate. Here a mass of folk, pressing out of the three great roads that met at this place, were held back by a crowd of sweating fellows from the farms, surging in through the gate, laden with fruits and vegetables, wood and charcoal, rice, beans and pigs; all to be used or devoured in the teeming city. Through this confusion of people Chang would force his way, crying his wares at the top of his voice. Not for him were the quieter streets where a man might saunter at ease. It was where men gathered thickest that he had to seek his customers.

One morning, as he struggled along in this fashion, an ancient man, wrapped in a tattered gown, thrust a bare arm out of his rags and touched Chang upon the shoulder.

"Young fellow," he quavered, "will you sell me enough tobacco to fill my pipe?" And from under his garment he brought out the kind of long pipe, with a small bowl, that was commonly used.

Chang stopped and looked for some clear space in which to set down his load, but the crowd was so thick that he could not find one. The old man showed him three copper pieces; because this was good payment for such a small amount of tobacco, Chang motioned for his customer to help himself.

The old man took a fill of tobacco and put it into his pipe. Then he took another, picking it up very deliberately between his thumb and forefinger and pressing it carefully into the little pipe bowl. This was more than Chang had expected the pipe to hold, so you can imagine that when he saw his customer helping himself for the third time his amazement was extreme. But that was only the beginning. The old man pressed more and more tobacco into his pipe. It never seemed to fill.

Loaded as he was and filled with astonishment, too, Chang could do nothing but stand and gape at these ruinous proceedings.

The old man did not stop until all Chang's supply of tobacco had disappeared into that apparently bottomless pipe. Then he pressed the three copper pieces into Chang's hand, lit his pipe with an air of great contentment, and with a mocking smile, disappeared into the crowd.

Disgusted and depressed, Chang flung the three miserable copper pieces into his tray and began to push his way toward his home, in a bad temper.

Ill success makes the load heavy, he told himself as the basket, swinging behind his back, seemed to get heavier and heavier. It was soon so much of an effort for him to carry it that he had to stop and put it down. He looked at it irritably, and then with wonder. It was nearly full to the brim with copper pieces, and even as Chang gazed, the heap of coins seemed to be growing larger and larger.

With a quick jump, Chang seized it in both arms, and running and staggering, just managed to reach his home with it before the growing weight tumbled him over the threshold, and he fell sprawling into his storehouse.

However, he was on his feet again in a moment, and breathing hard with excitement, began to gather up the copper pieces and put them into the stout box where he kept his money.

When he had done this he felt it was time to give some serious thought to this matter, so, standing in the street outside his doorway, he lit his own pipe and began to go over in his mind the curious events of the morning. But he had not taken more than three long puffs when he heard a small sound of chinking behind him in the store. Upset as he still was, he scurried back inside, with an alarmed face, only to find that the copper pieces had now filled his money box. The lid was pushed up, and coins were dropping one by one onto a heap on the floor.

Chang scratched his nose, and then ran and fetched a corn bin and began to fill that. It was a busy morning. Not until three corn bins had been crammed did the coins seem to stop multiplying.

The tobacco peddler was now a very happy man. He had so much money that he decided to give up this business of selling tobacco in the streets. He would use some of this money to buy a fine pawnbroker's business, and then every day he would be able to sit in his own shop, with dignity.

And this he did. He spent all the coppers in the three corn bins in doing it. But when it was done he prospered and was happy, especially because the money box, no matter how much he took out of it, was always full.

One morning an old man shuffled into Chang's shop with a few things he wished to sell. They were not of any particular value, as Chang saw at once. They were worth perhaps one hundred copper pieces.

Chang picked them up one by one and looked at them with sad frowns, as pawnbrokers must; then, coughing sympathetically, he asked the old man what price he wanted for them. The old man did not say "Ah" and "Oh" or hesitate for a moment. "Three copper pieces," he said, as if that were a lot of money.

Chang found it difficult to hide his astonishment; he had not been a pawnbroker for very long. But he managed to keep a grave face, and taking three copper pieces from his money box, he handed these to his customer, with a polite bow. Then, sweeping the old man's poor possessions into a bundle, he carried them into the back of the shop.

When he came back he half expected to find the old fellow still there, having perhaps changed his mind about the price. He had seemed to be a very casual, absent-minded person.

But no. The man had gone. And from that day the coins in the money box stopped growing. Henceforward when Chang took ten coins out of it, there were ten less left there. And if he again took ten more, why then there were twenty less.

I think the old man had taken back his three magic copper pieces.

The Long Nose

L ONG ago, there were two brothers, who lived with their widowed mother. Surely good fortune and success had passed them by. They were so poor that, too often, they had not enough to eat.

The old mother did not fail to lament their hard lot. "Ayee-ah!" she would bewail. "I'm sure that if matters do not mend themselves, we will be better off dead than dragging through life in this miserable way. What does it matter to me? I am old, and have no more use for the world's pleasures. But both of you have your whole lives before you. I can't think why you don't bestir yourselves and set out in the way of making money. Look at our neighbor Chen. He has all the food he desires and servants to wait upon him. When he goes out, he doesn't toil through the dust. He has a carriage. That's the way to live, I say."

The elder son would answer her mildly. "What you say is true, Mother. Neighbor Chen is rich and happy; no doubt because he worked hard in his youth. But how is one to begin? Even to steal chickens, one must first have some rice to entice them with."

One day, after such talking, the elder son Li Ta said to his mother, "Mother, I have a plan. Neighbor Chen has much money. Would he not lend us, perhaps ten dollars? What would ten dollars be to him? If this could be, then Brother Hsi and I could leave two dollars with you to support you, and go with eight dollars to seek our fortune. Surely with such a sum of money in our hands we should be able to make some profit."

The old mother thought that this was a very good suggestion. She went herself to speak with Neighbor Chen. He, good man, willingly lent this Li family ten dollars.

Then all was bustle and excitement in the small Li house. Elder Brother Li Ta left two dollars in his mother's hands, and went out and changed the eight dollars into eight thousand coppers, which he put in a bag. Young Brother Li Hsi looked hungrily at the bag. He had evil thoughts in his mind.

Next morning, very early, the two brothers set off. The younger brother Hsi carried the luggage, and the elder brother Ta carried the bag of coppers.

The wicked Hsi did not like to think that his elder brother was carrying the money. "That bag must be too heavy for you," he said, after they had traveled only a distance of perhaps five li. "Let me take it from you. You shall carry this luggage, which is less weighty."

"On no account," said Ta cheerfully. "I am strong enough for it. Besides, it is fitting that the elder should bear the most weight."

Hsi pretended to admire his brother's good heart. But as they traveled on, Hsi suggested so many times that he should take over the bag of money that finally, rather than quarrel with him, Ta allowed him to take the money upon his back. So thus burdened, with Ta carrying the luggage, they resumed their journey.

In a very little time crafty Hsi began to complain of a pain in his stomach. He lay on the ground, holding himself with both hands, and crying out in pretended sickness. "Go quickly, good Ta," he entreated, "and get me hot water to ease this pain in my stomach."

Suspecting nothing, Ta hurried off, quite distracted, in order to fetch relief for his brother. When he had almost given up hope of finding aid, he saw an old woman working in a field. When he told her of his younger brother's sad condition, she hastened off and came back to give Ta a cup of hot tea.

With this in his hand, Ta quickly retraced his steps, but when he got back to the spot where he had left Hsi, there was no sign of him at all. Ta searched around, to make quite sure that younger brother had not rolled some distance in his agony, but he was nowhere to be seen.

Then Ta thought, Ah! Surely Hsi has recovered from his pain and has gone on to find me again. In some way or other we have missed each other. I will have to return this cup to the old woman, and then see if I can overtake him.

So when the cup had been returned, Ta took a firmer grip of the luggage, and with hasty strides went off in the direction in which Hsi should have gone.

But although he pressed forward as fast as he could, he caught no glimpse of Brother Hsi ahead of him. The afternoon passed. The sun ceased to burn his brow. Dusk came, and then a white moon flooded the land with cold brightness. Ta began to wonder where would he find shelter for the night.

Presently, however, a little off the road beside a grove of willows, Ta saw a pavilion. When he walked across to it he found it empty. It was called the Pleasure Haunt of the Immortals. It should be good enough for me, thought Ta.

So he went inside. The ground floor was dirty and littered, but when Ta mounted the stairs he found the first floor to be clean and well fitted for rest. He settled himself in a corner, and to keep himself warm, covered his body with some fine hangings off the wall.

Now this Pleasure Haunt was still being used by some of the Immortals, and Ta had not been asleep long enough to begin snoring when he was awakened by voices.

One of them was saying: "This is in no way pleasant. We have nothing here with which to divert ourselves. We have not even any food to eat."

Another voice said: "But that is not so. See, I have here a stick. If I tap this stick it will produce all manner of food."

There was the sound of a tap. Then several voices said at once: "What a splendid feast this is!" And Ta, still with terror, could hear loud sounds of eating and drinking.

When the Immortals had finished drinking and the sweet rice had been set out for each of them, one said: "Just to the east of this place there is a spring of water, but the water is so bitter that none can drink of it. Now I wonder why that can be?"

Another at once said: "It is simple. There is a green pine tree by the spring. If that were cut down and pulled up, a green snake would be found underneath it. When the green snake is killed, the water in the spring will be sweet."

Then a fresh voice broke in. "If one were to look west of this place, there is a bridge which workmen have been building for twelve years. I wonder why it is not finished?"

"I can tell you," said another. "There are four pots of gold buried under that bridge, as well as four pots of silver. Only when those pots of gold and silver have been taken away will it be possible to finish building the bridge."

At this point Ta, though frightened, fell into a deep sleep. It is possible that the Immortals were about to discuss matters too secret for his ears, and that a well-disposed spirit caused this slumber. However that may be, it is sure that when Ta awoke once more, day was already come. Sunshine was pouring in through the lattice; the door was ajar, and the Immortals had gone.

Feeling a great hunger, Ta rose to his feet, hoping that there might be some scraps of food left upon the floor. But there were none. There was only flung across a stool a crooked stick.

Thinking there was little to lose by it, Ta gave it a hard tap. Immediately, a lavish meal appeared upon the table. With an exclamation of joy, Ta sat down and ate and drank with great relish. But he could not help feeling sorry that his younger brother Hsi was not there to enjoy it with him. Where is Hsi now? Ta wondered sadly.

No doubt the best hope of finding Hsi lay in resuming his journey, so with the least possible delay, Ta set off again. The sun rose higher in the heavens; the sweet dew dried off the grass by the roadside; and the heavy heat of the day fell once more across the land. When Ta saw an old woman drawing water at a spring, it reminded him of how thirsty he was.

He begged her for a drink of water.

"This water is too bitter for any man to drink," she told him. "It is fit only for pouring upon the melons."

Ta looked round and saw, growing close by, a green pine tree.

"If you cut down that pine tree and pull up the roots," he said to the old woman, "you will find a green snake. Kill the green snake and the spring water will be sweet again."

The old woman knelt before him and thanked him warmly for this advice. She begged that before he went he would tell her the name of his family and the name of his village. He did this gladly, and hastened, thirsty, on his way.

The road turned westward. Soon he came to a bridge which was but three-parts built. A large number of workmen were laboring upon it. Ta asked one of them: "How long, tell me, has this bridge been building?"

"It must now be twelve years," said the workman glumly.

"Twelve years! And you have not yet finished!" exclaimed Ta.

"You may well be astonished," said the man, giving the unfinished parapet a pat with his hand, as if it were an old friend, "but no sooner have we almost completed it, than it falls down again."

Ta called to the other workmen, who flocked around him. "Underneath this bridge," Ta told them, "there are four pots of gold and four pots of silver. When these are removed, the bridge can be built."

The workmen were very glad to hear this news, and insisted on knowing the great name and the native village of this wise young man.

Ta then took his leave of these people and journeyed on. Not long afterward he recognized where he was, and in a short time he was home again.

First, of course, he related to his mother the whole story of his adventures and especially of his encounter with the Immortals. When his old mother began to look suspicious of his story, he stopped to give the crooked stick a smart rap, and the rich meal which instantly appeared silenced all his mother's doubts.

But even while she was eating the finest meal that she could ever remember, she could not help but weep to think of her poor younger son Hsi, who was lost and could not be found.

And what was the younger son Hsi doing during this time? There is no use in concealing the truth. He was squandering his stolen eight dollars in all manner of foolish ways. And while he ate and drank and made merry with this money, it did not once occur to him to feel sorry for the brother whom he had robbed of every copper and abandoned so shamefully.

At home, Ta and his mother lived for many years upon the food which the stick produced. And during this time the news of the bitter spring turning sweet, and of the unfortunate bridge being at last completed, reached the incomparable ears of the Emperor himself.

Ever alert to reward merit, the Emperor sent high officials to wait upon Li Ta and to confer honors and riches upon him. And besides these, Li Ta was presented with gold and silver from those who now enjoyed the sweet-water spring, and with the four pots of gold and the four pots of silver from the workmen who had at last built the bridge. He was a rich and honored personage. He married and lived in great dignity and happiness.

One day, among the press of beggars at his gate to whom he always gave alms, he recognized, blear eyed and famished, his younger brother Hsi.

With a shout of joy, Elder Brother Ta leapt upon Hsi, and despite his dirty condition, welcomed him warmly. Then he led him indoors, and after Hsi had been bathed and clad in fine raiment and feasted richly, Ta asked him innocently how he had fared all this time.

"You must have been greatly distressed to find that you had been parted from me and that I had none of the money," said Ta.

"You cannot even begin to imagine how upset I was," lied crafty Hsi. "The thought that you were not with me to share the excitement of turning our eight dollars into sixteen dollars and then the sixteen dollars into thirty-two dollars (and who knows how far we might have prospered?) quite took the heart out of my breast. I confess I had no zest at all for the business, and as a result, I merely turned our eight dollars into four dollars, and then the four dollars into two dollars, until I had but one dollar left. And that I spent quickly, before I could lose it too."

Hsi told this tale in such a wry, humorous way that Ta could not but laugh, and he asked no more questions.

Hsi looked enviously around the spacious apartment in which he had just dined. "You, Elder Brother, have, however, done excellently in business."

"Ah!" said Ta with utter frankness. "I did not make my money out of business."

"Indeed!" said Hsi encouragingly, leaning forward in his chair.

Then Ta told him all about his adventures.

Hsi was deeply impressed by the story. He secretly determined to visit the Immortals and get some good fortune for himself.

So on the first evening that he could get away from his loving brother's company without being questioned, he slipped off, and made his way as quickly as possible to the Pleasure Haunt of the Immortals. When he reached it, he went straight upstairs and concealed himself in the chamber on the first floor.

Evening came, and a small number of Immortals climbed the stairs and sat themselves down.

"It's such a tiresome business," said one, "having to carry our food here, and then to endure all the fatigue of cooking it. What a pity we cannot find who the rogue was who stole your crooked stick. Then we could have fine meals again without any effort."

"Ah!" said one, who seemed to have been the stick's owner. "No doubt the rascal will keep far from here. But still, perhaps we had better make a search now, as we always have done since my stick was stolen."

Poor Hsi heard the sounds of chairs being pushed back and of feet walking here and there; then, off was whipped the covering under which he cowered, and with a great shout, the Immortal who had discovered him whirled him into the center of the room by his nose.

"So this is the villain who stole my stick," he roared, and pulled Hsi's nose a little harder. But why spin the matter out? Let it be told quite simply that Hsi's nose was pulled and pulled until it was twelve feet long.

With what lamentations did Hsi return to Elder Brother Ta, and how grieved was Ta to see Young Brother Hsi with his nose wrapped around his middle to keep it out of the way!

Ta decided at once to go to the Immortals, to return the stick to its proper owner, and to hope that when they had punished him they would forgive Hsi and restore his nose to some manageable length.

But either Ta was late or the Immortals were early, for when Ta made to climb the stairs of the Pleasure Haunt of the Immortals, he could hear that they were already there in the chamber above him.

He could hear them laughing and talking.

"Well, that was a good jest last evening. I quite enjoyed stretching that villain's nose. I can't remember a nose which pulled so easily as that one."

"No doubt there would be some cure for that nose," said another of them.

"Indeed yes," said the first speaker. "If one had the crooked stick, for instance, one would only have to tap the stick on the ground while the man with the long nose spoke his own name. You tap twelve times, the man answers with his name twelve times; and the nose is reduced to its proper size."

Ta waited to hear no more. He hastened home and explained to Hsi (who had done nothing but sit and nurse his nose) exactly what was to be done.

Then Ta tapped the stick on the ground and Hsi answered, "Li Hsi."

Tap.

"Li Hsi."

Tap.

"Li Hsi."

After the twelfth time Ta stopped tapping. Hsi, who all his life wanted just a bit more than he was entitled to, pleaded "Once more."

Tap.

"Li Hsi."

Alas, he had gone too far. Instead of a nose of decent size, Hsi now had a dent.

The White Snake Lady

O N an afternoon when the summer sun blazed whitely out of a hot sky, a poor young student was returning to the great city of Hangchow after an aimless walk. The ground under his feet was hot; the grass banks beside him were white with dust.

He walked slowly, without any special air of haste, rather as one would expect a poor young student to walk on a day so hot and sun laden. He was a pleasant, dark-faced young man in a poor gown of faded blue cotton, the long skirts of which he held up in one hand to give his legs more freedom to move.

As he drew near the West Lake a little throng of people moving excitedly under the shade of tall willows attracted his attention. He went nearer and pressed into the crowd to see what was going on.

A rough, bold-eyed fellow was holding a beautiful white snake, pressing it to the dry earth with a forked stick. For the amusement of the onlookers he was tormenting it, pretending to let it escape, and then quickly catching it again. Proud of the interest he was arousing, the lusty fellow laughed loudly at the struggles of the white snake, and those who looked on patted each other on the shoulders for joy, and laughed with him.

The scholar (Hsu Sien was his name) felt a great pity for the helpless snake. His face darkening with anger, he glared straight at the tormentor, but this fellow looked to be too stalwart to fight with.

Hiding his rage, Hsu Sien, in a voice that trembled with scorn, asked if the man would sell the snake.

43

The fellow stood back in mock astonishment.

"Who is this young lad who desires to buy this pretty creature?" he asked, to the amusement of his audience.

Hsu Sien said nothing, but held forward in his hand the trifling sum of cash that was all he possessed.

It was more than enough for the crude fellow. He snatched it with a flourish, and gripping the snake in his huge hand, thrust it into Hsu Sien's arms.

"It is yours, great lord. Go and play with it yourself."

A little ashamed at having shown his feelings in public, and blaming himself for having squandered his money on such a whim, the student hurried away. When he had gone a safe distance from the little crowd, he bent down by the roadside and let the snake go free. With one twitch of its tail, the white snake was gone. Shaking his head a little regretfully, Hsu Sien went slowly on into Hangchow.

But (the truth must be told) this white snake was no ordinary one. When this event occurred, the snake was nearing the end of a life of exceptional virtue and goodness. As a consequence, it was not very long before she was transformed by the Emperor of Heaven into a semi-fairy. In this condition she assumed the form of a beautiful lady.

Willing to reward her for her good life, the Emperor of Heaven decreed that she be sent down to Earth to help the poor student who had once rescued her from torment and death.

On the way down to earth the white snake lady met another snake who also had been given human shape. This one had been a blue snake, and she, too, had led a life of virtue and goodness. However, in both of these respects she had been a little less deserving than the white snake; it was therefore promptly agreed that she should act as the little maid of the white snake lady.

This important matter having been arranged, the two of them arrived in Hangchow.

By what means they found the poor young scholar I do not know. But I am sure that he had only to catch sight of the white snake lady once to fall in love with her. For she was most attractive.

She was of a beauty hard to describe. Her pale face glowed as if a white flame shone through delicate silk. Her slanting eyes were black, and above them black eyebrows swept upward like swallows flying. Her black hair, piled high, sparkled with the jewels that fastened it. Beneath her long, white gown with its silver embroidery, her tiny, bound feet pattered like leaves in a breeze.

So, having said that they met, it is only necessary to remark that before very long Hsu Sien and the white snake lady were married.

And they were both very happy. If Hsu Sien could be kind to a snake, imagine with what joy he would cherish such a sweet wife. And the sweet wife, fluttering through the house, looking dutifully to Hsu for encouragement or correction, was the picture of joy. The pretty maid pattered everywhere, doing all that was necessary for comfort and tidiness.

The little household flourished. Hsu very soon began to prosper. Many people paid him large fees for his skill in writing and teaching.

All would have been well had it not been for the Taoist priest Fa-hai, a thin, mean, anxious person.

This priest had a magic mirror which revealed to him that the wife of Hsu Sien was in reality a snake. Most men would have thought What of it? and with a shrug of the shoulders would have let the matter be. But Fa-hai pondered and fretted and slept badly until he went privately to Hsu and told him the startling news.

One must not think too harshly of Hsu Sien. Even the most levelheaded of men would find it difficult to receive with unconcern the news that his wife was in truth a snake. But Hsu was an impulsive man. His first feeling was of horror: his next was of fear. He must run away. But whither? "With me, to the Golden Mountain Monastery," suggested the scraggy priest.

Without a word, Hsu Sien went.

Oh! the grief and despair when the white snake lady found her husband had fled! Her pale face wet with tears, she searched the streets of Hangchow, the pretty maid helping her with anxious love.

It was a long time before they gathered news that the husband had run away to the Golden Mountain Monastery with the priest Fa-hai.

At once, without stopping for food or rest, the white snake lady set off for the monastery. It was a weary journey to make on stumbling, bound feet, but the lady and her faithful servant at last toiled, exhausted, up the third broad flight of steps of the monastery and eagerly began to ask for Hsu Sien.

When at last the answer came that he would not see her, the white snake lady did not scream or wail. With a proud face, she turned and fluttered bravely, with tiny steps, down the unending stairways.

Through a far-off lattice Hsu Sien watched her go.

From the mountain, wife and maid went in dreary silence toward the city. As they neared Hangchow they drew aside into a clump of bamboo to rest themselves. The white snake lady's face glistened with tears. The pretty maid was saying vicious things to herself.

Suddenly the sound of pounding feet was heard, and almost before the two could rise to look, a man's figure hastened by.

The white snake lady uttered a glad cry. The figure was Hsu Sien, running, running as fast as he could, back to Hangchow.

The lady could not hope to overtake him on her little feet, but the lowlier maid, whose feet had never been bound, could run with undignified speed. She quickly overtook the remorseful Hsu.

He, of course, desired only to be forgiven. The sight of his wife, so bravely and politely leaving the monastery, had overcome all his fears. His emotion was so great that the embraced his wife publicly. What did he mind, now, if she had once been a snake? No doubt if she had once been even a toad, he would not now have cared at all.

The Five Tiger General

ONCE, long ago now, in the heavy gloom of a winter's afternoon, a woodcutter was chopping firewood on the mountainside. When he paused for a moment to wipe the sweat from his brow, he heard the sound of sad whimperings coming from a nearby thicket of bamboo.

Wondering what could cause such a pitiful noise, he laid his ax across his shoulder and made his way toward the sound.

When he reached the edge of the thicket, he peered between the tall bamboo canes, but could see nothing. Nevertheless, whatever was making the complaint was somewhere within. He could hear the whining more loudly now, as well the sound of distressed breathing.

With great caution, he stepped into the thicket. Four seasons before this the bamboo grove had been cut down, and when bamboo is cut with a slicing blow from a heavy knife, a piercing sharp dagger of hard wood is left sticking out of the earth. The floor of the thicket bristled with these keen spears.

He had not gone ten paces, stepping as delicately as a deer, when he saw, to his horror, a tigress. For a moment he could not move for fear. Then he perceived that the beast was harmless. A tall shaft of bamboo had pierced right through its hind leg. The tigress lay there on battered earth bright with blood. Her eyes looked desperately toward the woodcutter, as if begging for aid.

The woodcutter was very distressed at this sight. He hurriedly backed out of the thicket, and with quick steps made his way down the mountainside.

When he reached his home, he called respectfully for his mother. "Mother," he said, "I have just seen on the mountain a tigress wounded and in great pain. I beg you will come with me and help to free it."

"In a moment, Son," his mother called back. "I will get wine for the wounds. *Ayee-ah!* The poor creature . . ." and muttering about the world being full of misfortunes, she hastened inside to equip herself. She was soon ready for action.

Together, then, the two went back up the mountainside. There, while his mother soothed the tigress with soft words, the woodcutter carefully and gently lifted the leg off the horrid spike. When it was free, the tigress did not show rage or fear, but lay, breathing hard and looking up at her rescuers with the greatest friendliness.

For all that, the mother thought it prudent not to wait until the tigress was quite strong again. As soon as she had soothed the wound with wine, she patted the beast in a sympathetic way, and then, thinking it proper to end this interview with some polite remark, said, "Tigress, we are too poor to afford a daughter-in-law. One day you must bring my son a fine young wife"; with that she smiled in a leave-taking fashion, and bowing three times, followed her son down the mountain.

That very winter a young bride of rich family was being conducted over this mountain to the home of her future parents-in-law. In this wild country those relatives and dependents who protected her were heavily armed. The wind was rocking the mountain tops. Small, thick snowflakes were falling.

Suddenly there was a roar that silenced the wind. Five tigers, teeth bared, tails lashing, crouched in the path of the wedding band.

At once every one of the bride's protectors threw away burdens and weapons and fled. Only the bride was left, trembling in her red veils, in her gaily painted sedan chair.

In less than an hour the young woodcutter, opening his door

to a hard knock, found a beautiful young bride waiting outside, and behind her, as near to smiling as ever tigers can get, the five tigers.

It will be understood with what joy the woodcutter embraced his bride. They were married as quickly as matters could be arranged. And very happy was the little household. The girl was a good wife to the woodcutter and an obedient daughter to her mother-in-law.

But on the other side of the mountain the bride's father, a rich and proud person, soon discovered what had happened to his daughter. He complained bitterly to the magistrate, and one day the woodcutter and his mother were dragged before the court for the crime of having stolen the young bride.

In vain did the young woodcutter explain that the girl had been brought to him by tigers. The magistrate laughed in a dis-believing manner and ordered that the young man should be well beaten with bamboo staves. Then if he confessed, he would be punished, while if he refrained from confessing, he would continue to be beaten.

To prevent this, the mother cast herself at the magistrate's feet and begged that she might be allowed to call the tigers as witnesses. The day was young, and this suggestion seemed likely to provide some amusement; the magistrate agreed.

To the astonishment of everyone, within a very short time the old woman came back with five tigers. Within a moment the whole courtyard was empty of people. Only the old woman stood there in the pale spring sunshine, and the prisoner—his head bowed under the heavy wooden block—and the magistrate, who stood upon his chair, with the skirts of his robe uplifted.

"Did you . . .?" was all his shaking lips could manage to utter to the tigers.

The five tigers nodded distinctly.

It was enough. The mother and son and the little wife were free to be happy together again.

That very summer a barbarian army of amazing savagery invaded the land.

The Emperor's army, commanded by Tiger General Wu, was sent out to give battle to this intruder.

How many trained soldiers the Tiger General commanded I cannot tell you this long time afterward, but they were very many indeed. And over them, as his chief captains, the Tiger General had Thunder-in-the-Sky—Fu-Shan-t'ing, and He-Who-Deals-Death—Fang Ch'ang-hua.

The never-defeated army of Tiger General Wu wound slowly, like a long serpent of gleaming iron, down off the mountain onto the wide plain beyond. There, during a long morning of heavy heat, it assembled itself in companies to await the onslaught of the enemy.

The bowmen with the repeating arrows, the spearmen with their little round shields, the wild men from the western parts who fought with long knives, the hairy horsemen from the north, and all the splendid companies of fighting men were drawn up in strict array. Along the line of battle rode General Wu with his two captains. The General's face was wildly painted in black and red and yellow, to give him a fierce expression, and so were the faces of his captains. While the Tiger General stopped to summon each lesser captain in order to point out to him the painful consequences of any lack of bravery, Captain Thunder-in-the-Sky Fu twirled his two great axes, one in either hand, and Captain He-Who-Deals-Death Fang brandished his horrid, long, hooked javelin.

Meanwhile, behind the troops, the official magicians worked incessantly, casting spells which it was hoped would cause rainstorms and dust storms to assail the enemy. One senior magician was making arrangements to turn day into night at any convenient moment.

A little to one side of this group, those who discharged rockets and fireballs made their solemn preparations.

The enemy appeared—at first no more than a sullen cloud of white dust far across the plain. Then, under the dust, anxious eyes could see the black fringe of advancing creatures. The sullen sunlight glinted on distant spears.

The army of the Emperor awaited the enemy with patience. It was agreed that it would take the whole of the rest of that day for the advancing troops to form themselves into proper order. Perhaps there would be time for a few demonstrations of defiance, a few shouted insults, and then dusk would defer the battle until the next day.

So while the Emperor's army watched with indulgent interest, the barbarians drew to within a distance of perhaps a thousand paces. They were a rabble. Except that they carried various sorts of weapons, there was little to show that they were an army. Many of the soldiers, it was noticed, had even brought with them what looked like large hounds, which they led with chains, and more laughable still, others led odd, hairy beasts that waddled on two legs like men and continuously turned their heads this way and that.

While the enemy was in this disorganized state it seemed wise to impress upon them the brave spirit of the Emperor's soldiers. Therefore, on an order dinned out from the great brazen war gongs, the whole of the Emperor's army took three great steps forward; every weapon was waved boldly in the air; from every throat roared a great and frightening shout. This done, the soldiers took three great steps backward and awaited the effect of all this upon the coarse persons who opposed them.

On several occasions this maneuver had had the most gratifying consequences. Whole armies had fled at the sight and sound of it. But these barbarians were evidently too brutalized to appreciate it; as far as one could see, they took no notice of it at all.

Or was it because they were too occupied with their own plans? For almost as soon as the Emperor's troops had retraced their steps, the enemy, in an untidy mass, waving weapons which looked extremely sharp, rushed, without order or ceremony, straight at the Imperial Army.

No one was prepared for such an untidy move, but startled as they were, the Emperor's troops stood manfully to face the distasteful business of battle. The war gongs were sounded bravely. The banners of the captains were lifted up. The magicians were foaming at their lips.

The dust of thousands of onrushing barbarians blew in the faces of the Emperor's army. When it lifted and the surging enemy could be plainly seen, a howl of dismay arose all along the battle line. These vile men were leading wild animals into battle; savage dogs, great apes, lumbering bears and fire-spitting scaly creatures which could have been dragons.

The entire Imperial Army turned and fled. And if it should be said that none fled faster than Tiger General Wu, than Thunder-in-the-Sky Fu, than He-Who-Deals-Death Fang, let that not be said in condemnation, for it was natural, being mounted upon horses, that they should.

How can I describe the anger and alarm of the Emperor? I think he would have become completely distracted had not a quite insignificant official suggested that the young woodcutter and his tigers might be of help in this matter.

The Emperor was ready to try any device. The fighting men were strongly in favor of someone else's attacking the foe. And so the woodcutter was instructed to rid the land of this horde of invaders with their horrid, wild creatures.

It is needless to say that the young woodcutter did this with complete success. The savage dogs, the great apes, the lumbering bears and the creatures who might well have been dragons, had been content to bite and scratch at frightened soldiers, but mere mention of "Tiger" to these animals was enough to send them, yelping and grunting and hissing, in flight. And no doubt because there were five slavering tigers who attacked them, they and the uncouth soldiers who owned them ran away and disappeared across the wide plain five times as quickly as one would have thought possible.

The Emperor was pleased, very pleased. As a mark of his esteem, he bestowed upon the young woodcutter the title of Five Tiger General. And more than that, the young man was given a high place at court. So, to the happiness of the mother and son and little wife was added honor and riches.

The Three Dwarfs

WU TA-LANG was a dwarf and a very ugly one. But, like so many people who are not born with pretty faces, he had a very sweet nature and was kindly in his ways. His wife Kin-lien was a dwarf, too, although, unlike her husband, she was delicately beautiful.

They made a very agreeable picture when they walked abroad. Kin-lien wore a skirt of plum red with panels of rich blue, and over it a long blue tunic with long white sleeves. On her head was a turban of blue, and the red sash which bound it to her dainty head hung down over her shoulder. Wu was dressed more severely, in a gown of crisp, gray cotton which buttoned tightly around his neck. The tiny wife walked with pattering steps on her bound feet, and Wu stalked proudly, a little in front of her, frequently looking back at his wife with pride and lovingness.

One autumn morning, however, they did not walk abroad in their usual manner. Kin-lien sat, prim and cramped, in a wheelbarrow which Wu, with manly determination, was pushing along the rough track which led away from their village. A long, dry summer had brought drought to the land. On their modest farm the paddy fields, which should have shone golden with the rippling rice, lay hard and parched. Like so many others, this worthy couple was forced to leave its home to seek refuge with relatives far distant and perhaps more fortunate. Wu thrust with his feet and shoved the lurching wheelbarrow along. The wheel, purposely ungreased so that the noise would

57

scare away evil spirits, squeaked like a pen of hungry pigs Kin-lien, nodding with the violent movement, clung to her seat with both hands.

Perhaps the wheel did not squeak loudly enough, or was it that the Rat Goblins do not mind noise? However it was, it happened that two out of the five Rat Goblins noticed the departure of Wu and his wife. Now, as everybody knows, the Rat Goblins' sole pleasure is in causing strife and confusion among the black-haired people of the earth. These two goblins at once seized on a chance of doing mischief.

And so when Wu, sweating hard by now, had pushed the barrow perhaps some six li of the way, he saw approaching him, far away down the straight, white road, somethting that moved as slowly as himself. As the distance gradually became less, Wu could see that this was another wheelbarrow, being pushed like his own. As they drew closer, Wu stopped. He thought this meeting would be a good reason for a short rest and a little chattering, of which he was greatly fond.

He stood, puffing, resting on the barrow handles and looking at the oncomers. There were two of them. One, a man, was trundling this barrow along, while the other, a woman, crouched uncomfortably upon it.

Wu's mouth opened, and the nearer the strangers came the wider it opened. For the man was a dwarf and wore a gown exactly like Wu's, and his face had the amiable ugliness of Wu's face. Kin-lien, for her part, was bobbing up and down on her seat and uttering fervent spells in her shrill voice, for the woman in the barrow approaching was a dwarf, too, and wore a skirt of plum red with panels of rich blue, and over it a long blue tunic. Its white sleeves hung down over her hands. On her head was a turban of blue, and the sash of it hung down on the same side of her head as Kin-lien's did. There is little need to say that her face had exactly the same delicate beauty as Kin-lien's. The Rat Goblins had taken care to arrange their prank correctly, down to the last detail.

Both Wu and Kin-lien were too astonished and bewildered to say a word.

It was the stranger who first spoke.

He greeted the dumbfounded couple with grave courtesy. "My humble name is Ta-Lang," he told them, with a bright smile, "and I am of the family of Wu in the village that is just six li ahead of me. This is my wife Kin-lien." He bestowed a smile of great esteem and affection upon the false woman. "Will you be so gracious as to tell me your great name?" he asked, with another bright smile.

Wu shook his head hopelessly. "I do not understand even three parts of this matter," he said, "for I am Ta-Lang of the family of Wu in the village six li behind me, and this is my wife Kin-lien—"

"What stuff and rubbish is this?" shouted the stranger, his face going copper colored with excitement. "What roguery have we here? Are you trying to pass yourself off as myself, you old cheat?" and he advanced upon poor Wu with threatening gestures.

Alarmed at this quarrel, both women had got down from their barrows, and while the false woman moved toward Wu, to help if necessary in the attack upon him, Kin-lien flung herself in the path of the threatening man to prevent him from reaching her husband.

"Stay, I beg," pleaded Wu to his attacker (for Wu was no lover of strife). "Let us approach this matter with becoming calmness. Now, if it will help to clear up the matter, let me make it plain that I am Wu Ta-Lang and that this is my good wife Kin-lien." And he cast a look of love and pride upon the lady who was now nestling by his side.

"No! No! Dear husband!" shrieked the unhappy Kin-lien, who was now beside the stranger man. "It is I who am your devoted wife!" With this, she ran quickly and cast herself at Wu's feet. The other lady cast herself also at Wu's feet. *"No! No!"* she cried also. "It is I who am your devoted wife!"

Poor Wu stood, completely perplexed, looking first at one and then at the other, and shaking his head till his cheeks trembled.

The stranger beckoned him in a more friendly manner. "Perhaps a word alone together," he said. He drew Wu a little off the roadway behind a screen of willow trees. But when they were there the man, to Wu's wonder, did nothing and said nothing. He simply detained Wu in that place for a few moments by smiling brightly at him, and then led him back onto the road again.

As they returned, both women ran and flung themselves at the feet of the stranger. "It is I who am your devoted wife!" they both screeched. Wu, left alone, stamped upon the ground with rage.

It could not be expected that this grave disturbance could take place without attracting some attention; first one passer-by, and then another, and a third, stopped to enjoy the beautiful noise and to marvel at this confusion of people. Each in turn tried to help, but their questions and suggestions only made matters worse.

It was not long before Wu himself began to wonder who he was. He could be seen wandering unhappily from person to person, saying, "I am Wu, am I not?"

Finally a plaster imagemaker, a man of sound understanding, came up and said, "Surely this is a matter which should be taken before the magistrate."

All who were there applauded this suggestion, the two disguised Rat Goblins louder than the rest (though do not ask me now which were which, for I cannot tell, myself).

When the party, hot and tired and very quarrelsome, arrived at the magistrate's court, it was to find that the magistrate himself was a dwarf. He was highly displeased at having this ridiculous case brought before him. He strongly suspected that this thing had been contrived to make fun of him.

And so, after his angry questions had succeeded in making

matters still more confused, he completely lost his temper and ordered all four to be beaten in turn. For, he argued to himself, one of them may cry out some matter of truth under the beating, and if none do, well, one might as well listen to them lamenting as to their shrieking against one another.

But happily, in the way that matters do sometimes fall out for the best, the talented Judge P'ao passed that way, and hearing the commotion, sent an official to find out what was happening in this mean village. When he was told, the judge alighted from his sedan chair and went into the court, his officers crying his name and dignities before him.

The magistrate bowed so low that he became quite giddy. Judge P'ao sternly asked for the facts of the case. When he had heard of the mixed state of the four apparent husbands and wives, he suspected at once that this was a trick of the Rat Goblins. Naturally a judge of such eminence and long experience would not be ignorant of their mischiefmaking.

He looked at the four persons before him for a long time, in silence.

Then he said, "Now this is a case in which I shall at once send for the Chief of the Taoist Magicians. I suspect that Rat Goblins are mixed up in this matter. The magician's miraculous mirror, if held up before a Rat Goblin, however he may be disguised, turns him at once again into his proper form of a rat. And I will ask the Chief Magician to bring with him the Cat God, who will enjoy a little sport with these rats."

Before the judge had finished speaking the Rat Goblins had disappeared. In front of the judge there now stood only Wu and his pretty little wife Kin-lien. The judge dismissed them kindly, and the whole village escorted them to their wheelbarrow and cheered them on their way with journey-encouraging cries.

Judge P'ao smiled a quiet smile as he heard their squeaking barrow trundle away. Whether there really was such a magician with such a miraculous mirror, only the judge could say.

The Royal Monument Pavilion

O NE summer morning, before the day was heavy with heat, Wang You-tao, a young man of good social position, set off on the journey from his village home to Peiping, to sit for the Imperial examinations. Success in these examinations was the way to high office and to other good fortune.

As the litter on which he was carried by four hurrying servants went jogging away down the white road, his young wife Ming Yu-hua stood, looking lovingly after him.

On the journey Wang's thoughts dwelt now upon his pretty wife and now upon the difficult examinations which lay before him. He wished greatly for success in Peiping, but he felt sad and anxious at leaving his wife. The truth is that Wang You-tao was an extremely jealous young man who could not bear the thought of leaving Ming Yu-hua, for even a moment, unshielded by his suspicious protection.

In this matter he was quite unfair to his loving wife, who had no thought of enjoyment other than pleasing her husband.

Almost as soon as the litter with Wang in it had disappeared from sight, a messenger from Ming Yu-hua's old father arrived at the Wang house. He carried a request that Ming Yu-hua would go to her parents' home to join in worship of the family's ancestors.

For companionship, a young sister of the husband was staying with Ming-Yu-hua, and to her the little wife went with news of this invitation. Ming Yu-hua did not think that she ought to leave the house in her husband's absence. The young sister, on the other hand, pointed out that she owed a grave duty to her parents and ought not to refuse to join them in such solemn duties as speaking with their ancestors.

63

In the end Ming Yu-hua agreed to go, but she insisted on returning before nightfall.

So off she went. The way was not long, perhaps thirteen li, as far as a man might travel in two hours without too much haste.

When the ceremonies in her parents' house were completed, she insisted on departing, despite her mother's wish that she should spend the night at her old home.

Full of good intentions, Ming Yu-hua hastened back toward her husband's house. It was evening now, and the light was getting dim. Behind her, black clouds were piling up in the sky and tumbling over each other, as if dragons were sporting in their midst.

Suddenly there was a livid flash, and then a clanging peal of thunder, and not a moment later rain came pouring out of heaven until one could scarcely see a man's length ahead.

Ming Yu-hua, frightened by these shocks, saw to her relief that just beside her on the road's edge stood the Royal Monument Pavilion. Though it had no side walls, it had a wide, stretching roof, and she was pleased to be able to stand under its shelter and listen to the roar of water and the clamor of the thunder.

Not many minutes later Ming Yu-hua heard the patter of running feet, and another person hurried gratefully under the shelter of the Royal Monument Pavilion. She could not see who this might be. The black clouds had sent darkness over the land.

The newcomer was, in fact, a young and unsuccessful student whose name was Liu. On three separate occasions Liu had presented papers to the Board of Examiners in Peiping. Each time he had failed. Nor was there any misfortune in this. His papers had been so bad that each time they had been placed right at the bottom of all the papers which had been submitted. Now he had just tried again, for the fourth time.

Perhaps he was unhappily thinking about this as he sheltered there from the storm. However, in a moment a flash of lightning, which made the neighboring trees stand forth as if carved in

jade, permitted him to see that he was not alone in this shelter. There was a lady, obviously young, standing quite close beside him.

Liu was frozen with dismay. It was in the highest degree improper to be alone with a lady in such a place as this. The fact that Liu was more than usually polite in his manners made him feel this even more keenly than most would have. His first impulse was to go away and get as far as possible from such an embarrassing situation. But then he realized that he ought not to leave this lady quite unprotected. As soon as he had recovered from the first shock he therefore decided to take up a position distant enough to be respectful, but sufficiently near to be of some protection.

Unhappily there was no place in the pavilion far enough away for the first, and no place outside it near enough for the second. Liu therefore found it necessary to stand just under the eave of the roof, in which place he was far enough removed to avoid offending the lady, but near enough to rush to her assistance if there should be need.

You may be sure that Ming Yu-hua was grateful for this delicacy of feeling. She stood, waiting patiently for the storm to pass over; and Liu stood, shivering with cold, as cascades of water poured unendingly off the roof over his head.

Now the Four Sentinel Gods, whose duty it is to note down worthy actions as well as unworthy ones, did not miss the honorable conduct of the unsuccessful scholar Liu. Though Liu, half drowned by now, but steadfast in his good purpose, had no idea of it, his unselfish deed was recorded. The Sentinel Gods wrote down every particular of his excellent conduct, even to ending their report with the words, "in spite of spouts of rainwater which descended continually upon his head."

As quickly as it had come, the storm passed. At one moment the wind roared and the rain drummed on the roof; at the next there was a sweet silence in the heavens. Relieved of his duties, the devoted Liu, taking care not to embarrass the lady by so much as one glance at her, hurried away, squelching and sodden. Ming Yu-hua looked after his fleeing figures with amused gratitude, and then sought her own way home.

When she was safely there, she could not resist telling her husband's young sister of the praiseworthy conduct of the unknown youth.

The slow summer days passed by until, late one evening, the master returned. Wang You-tao was in great good humor. He had been successful in the Imperial examinations. He would henceforth be one of the great ones of the land, and his wife would be an honored lady. The small household was a very merry one that evening.

The next morning his young sister, intending no harm, told him as a jest the story of Ming Yu-hua's encounter with the well-conducted young man. Wang gave no sign of the wrath and anguish that this story caused him. His jealous mind at once told him that his wife loved him no more. So he smiled with great gaiety to cover his rage, and occupied his mind with thinking what should be done in such a case.

For three days he went about his house, apparently without any cares upon his mind. On the fourth morning he called out kindly for Ming Yu-hua to come to him.

When she was there he said, "Little Wife, I have some small matter of business with your honorable father. Please go to him and greet him well from me and give him this letter, which explains what I have in my mind in the matter."

"I will go gladly, master," said the little wife, with a loving smile.

"Go quickly then, and fare well," he said.

With one of the servants to attend her, Ming Yu-hua was soon on her way. Wang stood where he could not be seen and watched her going. There was a smile of anger upon his lips. The letter she carried, addressed to her father, was an announcement that Wang was not satisfied with her conduct as a wife, that he wished to have no more to do with her, and therefore returned her to her father.

This business done, Wang then left to return to Peiping, where, since he had been successful in his examinations, he hoped to learn in what particular way his talents were to be employed.

When he had arrived there and arranged for his lodging, he made a call upon the Chief Examiner, the official who would be able to tell him what his future duties would be. Many other fortunate candidates were there for the same purpose, so Wang had to wait with impatience for some hours.

When at last his turn came to approach the Chief Examiner, he found that highly esteemed official still questioning a young man who had just been interviewed.

The Chief Examiner was tapping impatiently upon his table with his long nails. The youth, an undistinguished-looking person, seemed to be at a loss.

"Then you can give no explanation," insisted the Chief Examiner.

"Honored Sir, I cannot," stammered the young man.

"Believe me, I do not wish to do you an injustice because of annoyance at your stupidity, trying as it may be. Your examination papers fell short of excellence in so many small respects that they were the worst I have ever seen. They were placed at the bottom of the pile of all the papers submitted. That was their rightful place. But when I returned again on the next day, they had been put on the top of the pile. I put them back at the bottom. On the next day they were at the top again. This strange thing happened three times." The Chief Examiner leaned forward and gave the young man a look of great severity. "There is no man who would dare to interfere with my arrangements in this matter," he said. "I am inclined therefore to think that some Great Heavenly Being, perhaps Chu I himself, must have done this thing on your behalf. And if this is so, then surely you must have performed some praiseworthy act, and it must be considered by the Heavenly Ones that your high moral worth fits you for official rank, notwithstanding your quite remarkable stupidity. Now, examine your memory a last time. Is there nothing you have done in your short life which would merit such reward?"

The undistinguished-looking student struck his head with his fist to assist his memory. Then he said, "Ah!"

The Chief Examiner leaned even farther forward. "Pray go on," he said.

"Honorable sir. There was one quite insignificant matter . . ." And then Liu (for of course it was he) went on to tell the Chief Examiner, in a shy voice, of his behavior at the Royal Monument Pavilion.

Poor, jealous Wang did not wait to hear any more. How stupid, how proud, how cruel he had been! With the briefest of bows, he escaped from the Chief Examiner's office and fled through the streets of Peiping. He was shouting loudly for swift-running bearers to carry him quickly to the house of his wife's parents so that he might ask forgiveness of Ming Yu-hua.

The Son of the Turtle Spirit

THERE was once a turtle spirit who lived in a small pond in the garden of a great lord. With his hard eyes he often saw the great lord's daughter walking in the private garden. He fell in love with her.

Though I am a turtle, he said to himself, I am a spirit turtle, so why should I not turn myself into a young man and marry this attractive girl?

And he did.

Not knowing that the young man was really a turtle spirit, everybody was very pleased with this marriage; the great lord, the beautiful daughter's mother, and most of all the daughter herself, for the husband was kind and generous, as well as being most handsome.

There was one curious thing about the husband. He always disappeared from his bedroom before dawn and did not come back to the house again until the evening. The great lord did not allow his mind to be upset about this. He told himself that doubtless his son-in-law had serious business—in the Emperor's palace perhaps—to occupy his time. The lovely wife did not fret about it either, for what her splendid husband did with his time was no affair of hers. Only the old mother bit her nails and wondered.

At last the old mother persuaded her daughter to tie a thread of red cotton to her husband's arm after he had gone to sleep.

The next morning the mother was tapping at the bedroom door before ever the young wife was awake.

"Has he gone?" the old mother asked eagerly.

"He has gone." And through the window led a trail of red cotton.

"Now we shall see where he goes," whispered the old mother in an excited voice, and dragging the reluctant girl with her, she ran out into the garden.

Instead of the thread leading away down the garden toward the gatehouse, as they had expected, they saw to their amazement that it went no farther than the small pond, where it could just be seen trailing down under the still water.

"My husband must see this," said the old mother very gravely, and though this was more than she would ordinarily have dared to do, she sent servants to awaken the master.

When the great lord came and was shown what had happened, his heart was very heavy, for he had been proud of his fine son-in-law. "This can only be a turtle spirit," he said. "It must be the turtle which my father put in that pond."

Then he called loudly for some servants, and when they had come he ordered that they should empty the pond at once. When they had done this, lying there in the black ooze was the turtle. And the red cotton was tied to one flipper.

With a cry of anger and sorrow, the great lord leapt down beside the turtle and cut off its head. He told the servants to throw away the body. Then, shaking his head in misery, he went back into his house.

Bereft so suddenly of her husband, the young wife might well have pined and fallen into a sickness had it not been for the little son who was all that was left of her fine marriage. He was so handsome and quick and loving that she was able to find some pleasure in living, in spite of her sad fate.

One day, walking as she still did in the garden, she came upon the remains of the turtle spirit, where the servants had thrown them. Everything had moldered away except the bones.

Well, said the young woman to herself, turtle or not, he was at least my husband. I think it would be only respectful if I were to keep his remains in a reverent manner. So she gathered up the few bones and put them into a fine, silken bag, which she hung at the head of her bed. One day, she thought, there will come an opportunity to give my husband's bones a suitable burial.

The boy grew up to be very lively and high spirited; so much so that even when he was eight years of age he still had no schooling. He liked only to run about the streets and seek boyish adventures.

The old lord had died, and the old mother did not live long after him. There was now little money, and the boy's mother was forced to weave in order to feed them both. She often felt anxious about her son's future. He was so headstrong and carefree. She could not easily imagine him applying himself seriously to the business of life. Then she would lay down her work for a moment and laugh tearfully. Why must I be uneasy about such things? The lad is only eight years old. There is time yet for improvements.

But there was one anxiety which she could not wipe away as one might wipe away the unbidden tear. This concerned the bones of her turtle-spirit husband, which she still kept in the silken bag. As everyone knew, a proper burial was of the utmost importance for the welfare of a soul in the other worlds. And moreover, the better the place of burial, the better would fare the sons and grandsons of the dead. The mother was therefore very anxious to be able to afford to bury the turtle spirit's remains as soon as possible and in the most favorable place.

One day a man, whose business it was to seek out suitable places for burial, discovered what he felt sure was a remarkably favorable site. Through the city ran the great river, very fast, vastly deep, and disturbed by many violent eddies. Just above the city a confusion of currents had led to the deposit of a bank of mud in the middle of the river. This bank had gradually assumed the shape of a dragon, a most auspicious thing. It was complete, with head and two prominent horns and long, curled tail. And the head, as the heads of all the bridge dragons do, faced upstream. Nothing could be more propitious.

The grave seeker at once went to a rich man and pointed out to him the unique advantages of this almost magical burial place. The rich man willingly agreed with him. There could be no doubt that the sons and grandsons of any person whose body was buried in that dragon island would prosper excessively.

This rich man had been carefully saving the bones of his grandfather for just such an opportunity as this, and he was therefore eager to take advantage of the grave seeker's find.

But a difficulty presented itself. The dragon island was in the river's midst. Neither he nor the grave seeker knew of anyone rash enough to attempt to swim across to it. And of course no boat could live in those tumbling waters. They both scratched their heads, the rich man in perplexity, the grave seeker a little ruefully, for he feared that he might not get the large fee he had hoped for. It was in vain that they scratched. No answer came.

Unwilling to lose this good business while any chance at all remained, the grave seeker made a suggestion.

"Would it please you to post a notice," he said, "promising a large reward to anyone who will swim across and deposit the bones of your venerable grandfather in the dragon? It may be that there is some stout fellow who shall do this thing."

Although not very hopeful, the rich man saw that this plan might get him what he desired, so he gave an order for this to be done. A notice was drawn up, offering one thousand pieces of gold and one thousand pieces of silver to any person who would deposit the casket containing the bones on the dragon mudbank. This notice was hung conspicuously, and a watchman was set beside it so that it might not be misused.

When the people saw this notice, there was much laughter and some mocking. "Of what use would be one thousand pieces of gold and one thousand pieces of silver to a drowned man?" was a question which many asked.

The turtle spirit's son, playing nearby, heard the laughter and comments, and was drawn toward the notice. "What does it say?" he asked a seller of sweetmeats.

"What is that to do with you, little fellow?" said the man, not unkindly. When the boy persisted, the sweetmeat seller read the notice to him.

"I should like one thousand pieces of gold and one thousand pieces of silver," said the little boy loudly. At this all those who stood around laughed, but while they were still laughing the boy reached up and tore down the notice.

The watchman marched up to him, ready to give him a beating for such naughtiness, but, running out of his reach, the boy called out, "I can swim the river. I can swim the river."

"What, you? A boy of eight years or less?" growled the watchman.

"If I could not do this thing would I tear down the notice?" demanded the boy quite firmly. The watchman did not know what to do. It would be best, he thought, to get away from these mocking people, so, telling the lad that in that case he had better come and speak with the master, he led him away to the rich man's house.

The rich man and the grave seeker were very surprised to see so young a child in answer to their poster, but as they had not really expected any reply at all, they perhaps took the lad more seriously than they might otherwise have done.

They questioned him strictly, but he seemed so confident that they decided to let him try.

"But first I must go and tell my mother," he insisted.

So with reluctance they let him go. And when he had gone, the rich man looked at the grave seeker, and the grave seeker looked at the watchman. And the rich man said, "Let us now have something to eat and something to drink." For they did not expect to see the boy again.

The boy went running to his mother with the news. At first she was inclined to forbid this grave adventure. But then she thought, Well, after all, he is the son of a turtle spirit. No doubt he will be well skilled in swimming. And then she suddenly re-membered the bones of her husband. Surely a burial in the river dragon would be the most fitting of all for the remains of a spirit turtle? So, bidding the boy wait, she hastened indoors and re-turned with the bones of his father in the silken bag. "Take this, Son," she said. "And when you reach the island, place these bones in the dragon's mouth."

This promised, the boy sped away again, and soon surprised the rich man by returning to do his task.

The rich man and the grave seeker instructed him earnestly as to what he should do. Then, with the casket enclosing the grandfather's bones and the silken bag which contained his father's, the little lad confidently plunged into the torrent.

Naturally the waters presented no difficulty to him. With the agility of a turtle, he dived down deeply and did not come to the surface again until he had gained the bank of mud. He could see at once how exactly like a dragon it was formed; in the welter of waters its jaws seemed actually to open and close. So, pausing for the right moment, he popped his father's bones into the dragon's mouth while it was wide open, and watched as the mouth seemed to close and the throat seemed to swallow them. Then he hung the bones of the grandfather onto one of the dragon's horns, and without much exertion, swam back to the river's bank.

The rich man was highly pleased with this prompt service. Without any hesitation, he counted out one thousand pieces of gold and one thousand pieces of silver, and sent the boy, with two of his servants to carry these riches, home to his mother.

You can imagine with what joy the poor mother received her son and this lavish reward.

And was it true that the sons and grandsons of those whose bones were buried in so well-omened a spot became prosperous as a result? Yes, indeed. For the turtle spirit's son became more handsome and wiser than other men and finally became Em-peror. And the rich man's son was his chief minister.

The Man Who Sold Thunder

A YOUNG man of excellent character lived with his old
mother. His name was Tung Po-hua.

His mother was very fond of pig's liver, so Tung never
failed to go to the market early each morning to buy some for
her. Here he often met another young man, who came there to
buy pork chops, because his mother liked them so much. This
one's name was Kuo. The two soon became firm friends.

Now Kuo was not only an official in the court of justice, he
also kept a wine shop. And of course friend Tung came there
often to drink. If Tung had no money, he used to owe for his
wine, and this went on until the debt was so large that poor
Kuo could carry on his wine shop no longer.

Tung was very sad that, through his fault, his friend Kuo
should be brought to such a pass. However, such were Tung's
virtues in other respects that he was eventually to become one
of the Immortals. At this time he was far from attaining such
a condition, but he was already a magician.

To repay Kuo, he advised him to sell the wine shop and to
buy oranges with the money. Kuo could see no good reason for
doing this, but because Tung was his friend, he did what he was
told. He sold all his wine and filled the casks with oranges.

That very year a vile plague broke out in the city where they
lived. Nothing would cure this illness except oranges. They
brought such a high price that Kuo quickly became a rich man.
The two friends were very happy.

Then one night an Immortal appeared to Tung in a dream.
Tung had now so far perfected himself that it was time that he
went to join the Immortals. He was to meet his dream visitor

at the New Bridge on a certain day, to be escorted to the Land of the Blest.

Tung went to say farewell to his friend Kuo, and asked him to take care of his old mother. Then the two young men embraced each other, wept together, and parted.

On the proper day Tung waited for the Immortal at the New Bridge. When the Immortal arrived, he pointed to the rushing river and instructed Tung to plunge in. This Tung did without hesitation. He felt the keen coldness of the water as his head clove the surface. He saw the green darkness of its depth. And then, before he had time to feel fear, he was walking in a beautiful countryside where flowers nodded and sweet birds sang and the sun shone gaily in the heavens.

With his guide, Tung walked happily in this agreeable land. But without warning, as they followed a path, a great tiger crouched in their way, its tail twitching with evil intentions.

Tung started back, his mouth wide with fear, but his guide quietly told him to walk up to the tiger.

With an effort Tung did so, and to his immense relief, the tiger suddenly was no longer there; Tung was walking with the Immortal in a cool, green forest where a gentle wind whispered high up in the treetops.

They went on without effort and with no feeling of tiredness, through the cool, green forest shade until, ahead of them, Tung heard a crackling as of burning fire, and saw in the distance the fitful glare of flames. The smell of wood smoke was in their nostrils as they advanced. Finally they found themselves walking under a pall of smoke from out of which a shower of glowing ashes fell. Then, right across their path, Tung saw a great blaze which stretched to right and to left of him, as far as he could see. The heat was hardly to be borne, and Tung quickly ran back to a safer distance.

But his guide, plucking him sharply by the arm, told him to have no fear, but to walk boldly through the horrid flames. Eyes shut, hands before his face, Tung bravely rushed into the furnace.

The moment he reached the fire the scorching heat ceased, the roaring crackle stilled, and there was a coolness and a quietness. Tung opened his eyes. He found himself in a wonderful palace, so gracefully constructed and so richly adorned that he knew that he must at last be in the Land of the Blest.

And so he was.

He was entranced with the beauty of this place. It was so agreeable beyond all imagining that he could not help wishing that his mother could be with him to share his joy in it. He was very sorry now that he had not asked in the first place that his mother might come with him. There would have been no harm in it. She would have enjoyed this loveliness and peace. Indeed, the regret that his mother was not here was beginning to spoil Tung's pleasure in this Land of the Blest.

At that very moment the Immortal (who had gone away while Tung was discovering the fresh beauties of this place) reappeared. He wore a look of displeasure.

"You have not thrown off the love of Earth," he said sternly. "You are evidently not fit for this place. You must now return to Earth."

Even while the Immortal was still speaking, Tung found himself back upon Earth again. But he was not in the city of his birth. Instead of busy streets, he looked upon wild mountains.

The Immortal handed him a small stone. "I regret to say," he told Tung, "that you are some thousands of miles from your home. This stone must serve as money for your journey. If you are in want, you must cry out 'I sell thunder.' Then if any man wants to buy, you must write the word 'thunder' in the palm of his hand with this stone. When this is done, if the man opens his hand he will hear peals of thunder."

As soon as the Immortal had finished speaking, he disappeared.

So Tung, having nothing better to do, turned his face to the east, which was the direction in which the Immortal had pointed, and began to walk.

He walked for many years, but he did not suffer hunger on the way. If he were hungry, when he reached a village, he would stand and shout, "I sell thunder." People would come, crowding and laughing and chattering in response to such a strange cry. And when the first person had bought some thunder and everybody could hear the resounding crashes of it, everyone wanted to buy a little, just for the fun of it.

So Tung traveled quite happily, and at last he reached the city where he was born. His old mother was delighted to see him once more, and his true friend Kuo welcomed him with open arms.

And by selling thunder Tung continued to live.

One day the magistrate Hsuing was sitting in court in the city, trying the cases of those who were accused of crime. It happened that Tung had sold a great deal of thunder that morning, and many of those who had thunder in their hands were in the court to admire the wisdom and skill of the renowned magistrate. The open yard in which the court was being held was crammed with people.

By an unlucky chance, one buyer of thunder, without thinking, opened his hand. There was a loud peal of thunder. The magistrate stopped in the middle of a very long sentence and looked up, startled, at the sky. It was of a pure blue. No cloud was anywhere to be seen. The magistrate looked down keenly at the people crowded below him, to see if he could discover any mischiefmaker. Every face, as he scanned it, was both solemn and respectful. Shaking his head a little doubtfully, Magistrate Hsuing continued with what he was saying to a dishonest shopkeeper who was groveling before him between two big guards.

Through nervousness, perhaps, another buyer of thunder opened his hand. Thunder roared across the peaceful blue sky.

The audience could not help but laugh as it watched the be-wildered magistrate looking east and west and south and north to discover whence the thunder came. And while everyone laughed, those who still had thunder in the palms of their hands let it loose so that the courtyard rocked with the thunderclaps.

If the magistrate was very angry, who can be surprised at that? He was, in fact, in such a fit of rage that for the moment nobody's head was safe. To avoid unpleasantness of this kind, it was necessary to tell Hsuing that there was a citizen standing outside the court, selling thunder.

In one of the most quickly conducted cases that he had ever tried, the magistrate condemned the unfortunate Tung as a sorcerer and a troublemaker. Tung, with a heavy wooden collar clamped round his neck, was thrown into prison.

His friend Kuo, who was still connected with the court of justice, often used to visit Tung in prison, to bring him food and comfort. But there was little in the way of good news that Kuo could bring.

No pleading could change the iron will of Magistrate Hsuing. In vain was Tung's good character urged on his behalf; Hsuing regarded himself as insulted, and would not relent.

Then a revolt broke out in that province. It was a magistrate's duty not only to enforce the law but also to keep order. So Hsuing prepared to go at the head of the troops, to put down this rising.

Kuo, as an official, would go with him. When Kuo went to visit Tung in prison, Tung said to him, "The magistrate Hsuing will meet misfortune during this expedition. Please do not ac-company him."

Kuo said, "I am a court official. I must go." But his heart was troubled, for he knew that his friend had magic powers.

When Tung saw that Kuo was determined and would not stay behind, he said, "In that case, if you must go, please swallow this pill which will keep you from harm."

The magistrate and the soldiers went out from the city to

destroy the rebels, but Kuo could not go with them. He was very ill. It was the pill which had made him so, as Tung had intended that it should.

In two days news reached the city that the magistrate was dead. He and his soldiers had been ambushed by the rebels. Very few of the soldiers and none of the officials had escaped with their lives. So Kuo had been saved by Tung's pill.

Now that Hsuing was dead, it was possible to get Tung out of prison, and thereafter the two friends were able to enjoy each other's company in freedom.

The Dissatisfied Good Man

IN a village near Chengtu there lived a man who had a great abundance of riches. But he did not try to keep them all to himself, as he might have done. He delighted in helping those who were poorer than he was; nor did he expect great thanks for the kind things he did. Naturally such a man is much talked about, and the fame of this one spread far and wide, until even the Immortals in Heaven heard about his charitable ways.

One day two of the Eight Immortals thought they would test the character of this kindly man. I think they must have been K'ung-mu and Chang Kuo, because on the way to the village the one walked with the aid of a crutch, while the other rode a magic white mule. However, before they came very near to the rich man's house, they both went a little aside from the road, and by magic, changed themselves into dirty beggarmen. In this disguise, K'ung-mu retained his one crutch, but Chang Kuo, before transforming himself, folded up his mule, as if it were a piece of paper, and stuffed it into his wallet.

When these two beggars reached the house of the good man, they stopped outside the gate and began to argue, the one with the other. In a very short time they were giving each other nasty names, and when they could think of no more of these, they began to fight. K'ung-mu, hopping actively on one leg, dealt Chang Kuo many grievous whacks with his crutch, while Chang Kuo, who had seized K'ung-mu's beard, tried hard to overturn him with savage pulls. Such a din they made that the rich man sent a servant to ask the gatekeeper what was happening. When he was told, the rich man came out into the road himself. He did not shout abuse at the two fighters and order them from his door, but in the pleasantest manner he invited them to come inside and be his guests.

This suggestion quickly stopped the fight.

In the great house the two beggars were provided with new clothes and with fine shoes to replace their muddy straw sandals. Then they sat down to a splendid meal. I doubt if ever there were guests who behaved so badly at table as did these two. When fresh dishes were brought in, they did not wait for their host to invite them to taste them. They stretched out long arms and seized, without ceremony, anything that they fancied, and gobbled down each thing just as if they were animals. If they had been doing it on purpose, they could not have behaved worse. Their host, who through their greediness got scarcely anything to eat himself, made no complaint, but behaved as if he were well pleased with their bad manners.

When the meal was ended and it was time to go, the two beggars just sat dully, staring at nothing and acting as if this were their own house. The rich man tried to entertain them with a few remarks and a few questions, but the beggars either did not answer him at all, or did so in such an offhand manner that any other person would have had them beaten.

When it was growing dusk, one of the beggars said, "Well, Master. It is dark now. We cannot go on farther. Let us sleep here till morning comes."

To this the rich man pleasantly agreed.

Then how shockingly the guests behaved! Declaring that they were not warm enough, they put their own dirty clothes on over the fine ones which had been given to them, and, getting into bed like this—with even their muddy straw sandals on— they made a fine mess of everything. Not content with that, they sang loudly together the whole night through.

In the morning, after having eaten a good breakfast at the rich man's table, they went off with surly faces and without even one word of thanks.

If the rich man was glad to see them go, he gave no sign of it. He went with them to the gate with as much politeness as if they had been distingushed persons, and after they had left he had the mess they had made cleaned up, and never uttered a word of complaint against them.

The next morning, when he was in his garden, one of the maids tripped past him, carrying a bucket of water from the well. The rich man, wishing to make some remark, however silly, to a pretty maid on a bright morning, said: "What a pity it is that the well is not full of wine, instead of water."

The maid gave a little laugh and glanced down at the brimming bucket. Then she gave a loud shriek, for the bucket was full of yellow liquid which smelled exactly like rice wine. And when it was tasted, it tasted exactly like rice wine. And the well was always full of this valuable liquid.

So the rich man was able to sell rice wine more cheaply

than the wine merchants. Through this business he became richer still.

One day a customer who came to buy wine also asked for brandy. The rich man excused himself. "Alas! I have no brandy."

"What stupid thing is this?" asked the customer, in an ill humor. "You sell wine, but you do not sell brandy. I've never heard of anything so silly before."

The rich man was a little hurt at this. The next morning he stopped the maidservant as she hurried along with a bucket full of wine from the well. "I do wish," he said, "that all the wine in that bucket would turn into brandy."

It did.

So now the rich man was happy selling brandy, which cost much more than wine. And he became richer still.

It was not long, however, before a man asked him for grape husks.

"I'm so sorry," said the rich man, "but I have no grape husks."

"But if you make wine and brandy from grapes, you must have the husks that are left when the grapes have been pressed," protested the customer. "I never heard anything so ridiculous. No husks, indeed. This is a fine wine merchant!" And the customer went away in a huff.

It's a great pity not to have grape husks to sell when there are people who would buy them, thought the rich man to himself. I wish I had some grape hu—" He stopped suddenly. The two dirty beggars were walking toward him through the garden.

K'ung-mu, balancing upon his good leg, pointed his crutch at the rich man. "You are a kind man," he said, "and you have been very charitable, but you are too greedy. When you have wine, then you want brandy; when brandy is granted, you want grape husks as well. From now on there will be no wine and no brandy. There will not even be grape husks."

Chang Kuo had been listening and nodding his head while his

companion spoke. As soon as K'ung-mu had finished, both beggars vanished, and in their place stood the two Immortals. K'ung-mu turned around, without another word, and stumped toward the gate on his crutch. Chang Kuo, after a sympathetic glance at the rich man, hurried after him. The rich man followed and stood at the gate, watching wistfully as they went. The lame Immortal had hurried on down the road. Chang Kuo stopped just long enough to take from his wallet what looked like a folded piece of paper. He blew upon this with his mouth, and it unfolded at once into a white mule. Chang Kuo climbed upon it and clattered off down the road after the lame one. But as the rich man still watched, the two Immortals apparently tired of this slow method of travel, and a convenient cloud happening to pass by, they leapt lightly upon it, mule and all, and swept swiftly toward Heaven.

When the rich man looked fearfully into the buckets and into the well, he found only clear, sparkling water.

The Heavenly Spinning Maid

WHEN the Milky Way lies across the sky you may see, on either side of it, two stars. One, of a pale brightness, is called the Spinning Maid; the other, which twinkles more redly, is called the Cowherd.

Many thousands of years ago, in the court of the Emperor of Heaven, there was a little spinning maid. She worked so hard at her spinning and weaving, and had such a keen eye for color and pattern, that never before had such exciting materials been woven for the Great Heavenly Ones.

The Emperor of Heaven was of course highly pleased with the pretty maid, and wished to reward her. This was a matter on which he thought he would like his wife's advice, so he sent a command that the Empress should come to him. As fast as she could, swaying gracefully on tiny, bound feet, the Empress hurried before him.

When she had finished bowing, the Emperor opened his mind.

"I desire to arrange some reward for the little spinning maiden," he said. "Now in what way do you think we can do this?"

The Empress shook one slim hand free of the long sleeve of her yellow robe, in order to tap her head smartly, so as to encourage thought. She stood still, thinking hard, for so long that the Emperor began to shuffle his feet in impatience.

"I have it!" exclaimed the Empress at last, in a voice like tinkling glass. "It is difficult, because what reward can one give in Heaven where everything is to be had, and everyone is content? But a complete change, my lord, such as a short stay down there on Earth—"

The Emperor was so excited that his beard trembled.

"Excellent!" he shouted. "Splendid! Yes, a short stay on Earth will be just the right thing for her. Let me see, you could find her a suitable husband so that she is cared for? And let it be the time of spring, so that the Earth is reasonably attractive. And surely after a few weeks she will return refreshed, and no doubt full of new ideas for her weaving."

Saying that he would leave the arrangements to the Empress, the Emperor, in a good humor, dismissed her.

Before sending the spinning maid down to Earth, the Empress had to choose a husband for her; one who would support her and shield her from harm. Of all the young men down on Earth she chose Chen-li.

He was a strong, dark-faced, smiling young man. Both his father and mother were long since dead. Chen-li lived with his elder brother and sister-in-law on the tiny farm which was all their inheritance.

The farm lay on the banks of the peacock-blue river which runs shouting down into China from the Great Snow Mountains. The elder brother made a poor living off so small a farm, and life was hard.

A day came when the elder brother had to pack a great load of charcoal on to his back, to carry down to the City of Gwan Hsien. The journey there and back again would take him seven long days.

When he was gone, Chen-li was happy to do all the work of the farm himself. But as he went about his rice planting (for it was about the time of spring), his sister-in-law looked at him sourly. She could not bear the thought that one day this small inheritance would have to be divided with him, according to the custom. And as she followed his movements with angry eyes, the thought came to her that now, while her husband was absent, was a good time to arrange matters so that there would be no need to divide the property after all.

The thought had no sooner come to her than, with a lighter

heart and a cruel smile on her lips, she hurried off up the side of the mountain which towered above the farmhouse, to search for poisonous young leaves. And, to make more certain, she sought for poisonous roots as well.

So when Chen-li's breakfast rice was handed to him next morning, it had in it enough poison to kill five strong men.

Chen-li took it to the open doorway, where he could enjoy the sight of the sunrise while he was eating, and at the same time escape some of the smoke of cooking.

The elder brother's wife brushed quickly past him and went down out of sight to the river's edge, to pound the washing upon the boulders. In this way she thought she would avoid any unpleasantness.

Chen-li, in the doorway, was just about to begin his breakfast with his chopsticks, when his cow walked up to him. She was a poor-looking creature who gave little milk, but she ate very little and had friendly eyes.

She was a contented beast, not expecting much and grateful for the thin diet the farm provided. Her only complaint was of the behavior of the dog of the elder brother's wife, which was as vicious as its mistress. The cur's favorite amusement was in giving the cow a sharp bite when she was chewing the cud, or tearing hairs from the end of her tail when her back was turned.

As the cow approached, Chen-li welcomed her with a stroke of his hand on her neck, but the dog, which was lurking nearby ready to gulp up any dropped crumbs of rice, bared its teeth at her and growled and barked. Chen-li drove the bad-tempered cur back, and having done so, was astonished to hear the cow speak.

"It would be better not to eat that rice, Chen-li," the cow said.

Chen-li could hardly believe his ears. And then he realized that of course this must be a fairy cow.

"What shall I do with the rice, then?" he asked politely.

"Throw it to the dog," said the cow, for even fairies can sometimes bear a grudge.

Chen-li did so. The dog leapt greedily upon the rice, licked it all up, and died in a frenzy. Chen-li looked with startled eyes at the dead dog, and then turned and regarded the cow with great respect.

Of course his sister-in-law was both surprised and vexed when she returned to find her dog dead and Chen-li not only alive, but very cross with her for having tried so hard to kill him. In fact there was a nasty quarrel, and harsh words were said on both sides.

In the end, Chen-li shouted that he would no longer stay on the farm, and demanded his share of the inheritance before he departed. After some very hard bargaining it was at last agreed that he should take the cow. So, followed by this useful beast, Chen-li turned his back upon his birthplace and set off into the mountains.

As the two traveled amiably, spring seemed to go along with them. Bright canna flowers unfolded beside their path, and the pink of peach blossom overhung them. Butterflies, yellow, red and blue, as big as a man's hand, fluttered before them. It was a happy journey for Chen-li. It was the first time in his life that he had been free from heavy toil. He wandered carefree, full of well-being. Whenever he wanted anything, the fairy cow supplied it at once.

A day came when, in a beautiful valley, far from any habitation, Chen-li stopped. The sun shone upon fresh grass in a wide clearing amid the forest trees. The warm air hummed with happy bees.

"It would be good," he said, "to have a modest farm in this place. See, here is a clear stream to give us water; there is timber for all our needs; and this great mountain behind us would keep off the sharp winter winds."

The cow swished her tail happily. "It can be arranged," she said, and with grave eyes looked at the juicy grass.

"I shall need a plow—and a mattock—and an ax," cried

Chen-li, getting more excited with each thing he thought of. The cow nodded. It would be done.

"And a water wheel to raise the water from the stream onto the fields—"

The cow nodded again. "And you want pots and pans for cooking," she said. "And how fortunate! Here are some most convenient flat stones by the water on which the washing can be beaten out."

Chen-li's face fell. "Cooking? Washing?" he faltered. "But who is to do these things? I must busy myself outside on the land, sowing and planting and reaping. How are such things as cooking and washing to be done?" He looked hopefully into the cow's face, but the cow avoided his glance.

She looked carefully away into the trees, her nose wrinkled in thought. At last she said, "A wife could do these things."

"Of course!" shouted Chen-li, much relieved. "Of course! I must have a wife."

This was the very thing which the Empress of Heaven had instructed the fairy cow to arrange.

The cow pretended to be pondering for awhile. Then she said slowly, "Well, as good fortune would have it, there, just a short way down the stream, is a magic pool. In this pool fairy maidens often bathe. If you were lucky enough to grab the clothes of one of these maidens while she was in the water, she would, according to the custom, have no choice but to become your wife."

Chen-li, so anxious to have the matters of cooking and washing arranged for, was off before the cow had finished speaking. He followed the sparkling brook to the forest's edge. Then, parting the branches of a thick shrubbery of red blossom, he saw before him a dark pool whose waters splashed musically in all directions as a beautiful maiden plunged and swam.

Chen-li thought he had never seen anyone so pretty, and it is not to be supposed that he had, for this was the Heavenly Spinning Maid, and her beauty was more than human. He was so dazed by this sudden meeting that he quite forgot all his plans. It was the cow, who had prudently followed him, who brought him to his senses.

"Grab her clothes," she reminded him.

Chen-li leapt forward and seized a pile of pale silk which lay by the water's brim. The moment he did so the Heavenly Spinning Maid stopped splashing, turned around and saw him, and with a welcoming smile, said, "Young sir, if you will give me back my clothes, I will come with you and see to the cooking."

"And the washing?" stuttered Chen-li.

"And of course the washing," said the Heavenly Spinning Maid.

And how happily then the time passed for Chen-li and his beautiful wife and the cow. Chen-li carved out his fields, and sang as the seedlings burst from the soil. The Spinning Maiden cooked the tastiest dishes, and sang, too, as she went down to the water with the washing. The cow lay in ripe grass, with the sun warming her flanks, and cocked a contented eye at the summer sky.

And what had started in Chen-li's mind as a matter of cooking and washing very quickly changed in the company of his pretty wife. Before many days were over the two loved each other very truly, which was what made them so happy.

In fact, they were too happy. Day followed day; week followed week; month after month went by, and the Heavenly Spinning Maid quite forgot that she had work to go back to in the Heavenly Court. And the fairy cow did not choose to remember that the Empress of Heaven had told her to send the Spinning Maid back again after a little time. The cow was too comfortable to care.

The Emperor of Heaven was angry at this disobedience. On the seventh day of the seventh month he sent stern messengers to command the maiden to return to her spinning and her weaving.

She was heartbroken at leaving Chen-li, while he himself could not even understand what was happening. He stood, stiff with anger, as the Spinning Maiden and her dark attendants fled up into the sky.

He turned in desperation to the cow. "I must follow her!" he cried.

"It is granted," said the cow, without thinking. And in a moment the young man was flying up into the blue. How long he sped upward, who can tell? The light blue darkened. Constellations of stars parted before his coming. Ahead of him, up in the windless wilderness, the little group fled in the pale starlight. Chen-li was awed and frightened, but still he hurtled on in search of his lost bride.

The Empress of Heaven, who also had been very angry at the Spinning Maiden's long stay on Earth, was watching this chase with displeasure. She saw that Chen-li was likely to overtake the girl. So, with her thin lips parted in an angry smile, she flung her white silken scarf between them.

Chen-li stopped suddenly. Across his path the scarf lay, like a wild river in the sky, impassable. It flowed and shimmered in a torrent of white fire. From the other side, where the Spinning Maid stretched out her arms, a sad cry reached him. With his hands over his ears, Chen-li returned the way that he had come.

So the Spinning Maid went back to her work in the court of the Emperor of Heaven. And Chen-li sadly went back to work upon his farm. And the fairy cow had to do the cooking and the washing.

Of course, no sooner had the Empress of Heaven parted this young couple than she began to feel sorry for what she had done. Without losing her dignity, she naturally could not remove the stream that she had flung between them. To this very day the Milky Way hisses coldly between the stars.

But the Empress of Heaven did decree that once a year, on the seventh day of the seventh month, the young couple should meet up there in the sky for a happy reunion.

And you may still see the Spinning Maid in the sky on the one side of the Milky Way, and on the other the Cowherd. And if you should be looking at just the right time on the seventh night of the seventh month, then you will surely see the two stars meeting together again, just for a little while.

The Nung-guama

A POOR woman, a widow, went out of the city to take some cakes to her venerable parents.

She made what haste she could with quick, small steps on her tiny feet, for the way to her parents' village was long.

The dusty road was empty. Below it on either side stretched the fresh, green, paddy fields. As the woman was about to pass a thicket of bamboo, out sprang a Nung-guama—"Heh! Heh!"

There was no doubt that it was a Nung-guama, for it had a bull's body, a head as big as a wine jar, and its teeth gritted and its claws twitched. And there was no doubt that it was a man-eater, too, because of all things the Nung-guama delights most in human flesh. "Heh! Heh!"

No person relishes being eaten, be it by tiger, snake or dragon. But what strikes refined people as particularly horrid about the Nung-guama is his manner of eating. He does not pick delicately, disposing of morsel after choice morsel in a seemly way. He simply scrunches and tears in the most vulgar possible manner, and devours everything—hair, head, bones and all—uttering meanwhile his coughing kind of bark, "Heh! Heh!"

Less frightening, but still unpleasant, are his feet. These are extremely soft and floppish, so that as he goes about you can hear his fat feet flopping on the ground—*Flup. Flup.*

No wonder then that this poor woman sank at once to her knees in terror and hid her face from this terrible sight.

The Nung-guama, eyes gleaming redly, said greedily, "Give me all those delectable cakes."

Terrified as she was, the widow's duty to her parents came first.

97

"I can't do that," she sobbed. "They are for my honored parents."

"Very well," growled the Nung-guama. "Tonight I will come to your house and drag you to pieces with my claws and scrunch you up with my sharp teeth."

At that the widow uttered a quick shriek and cowered there in the dust. When, after a long time, she lifted her head fearfully and looked about her, the Nung-guama had disappeared.

But there was no doubt at all about his intentions. Certain of a painful and unseemly death when night should come, the widow sat in the dust, the cakes forgotten, holding her head in her hands and howling with grief.

Those who passed that way stopped politely to enquire what had upset her.

"The Nung-guama will come tonight to drag me to pieces and scrunch me up," she told them.

These other persons, hearing this, nodded their heads gravely and pursed their lips. So it would be, they told her; the Nung-guama would be sure to come.

While they were chatting thus, a passing peddler stopped to enquire why this woman was weeping so loudly. They told him.

He set down the bamboo baskets which hung from his carrying pole. "Here," he said to the widow. "I give you twenty sharp needles. You may stick them in the door of your house. Who can tell? Perhaps the Nung-guama will prick himself when he comes." And the peddler shouldered his burden again and went off.

The widow, still not comforted, continued to wail.

Her cries attracted a man who collected dung, which he used to spread upon his fields. He asked what her trouble was. When she told him, he considered for awhile and then said, "Here is a little dung. Spread it on your door. Perhaps the Nung-guama will dirty himself with it and go away."

The woman cried as loudly as before.

A man came by, shouting loudly, "Snakes to sell. Snakes

to sell." He stopped when he saw the lamenting woman. When he asked, she told him all that had happened, about the Nung-guama, the peddler, the man who collected dung. The snake seller wanted to help her. "Here are two of the most poisonous of my snakes," he said. "Put them in the water pot. It may be that the Nung-guama will want to wash his hands. If he tries to do so, these snakes will bite him dreadfully."

The woman thanked him, but even before he had gone she was weeping again.

There came then a seller of fish. "What is all this lamentation?" he asked those who stood around. While the widow howled with fright, he was told the whole story.

He offered the unhappy woman two round fish in a cooking pot. "Take these two round fish," he urged her. "Don't cook them, or they won't be able to bite. Keep them in the pot. Who knows? If the Nung-guama is bitten by the snakes, he will think that the cooking pot is full of hot water and safe for him to bathe his wounds in. If he does put his hands in the pot, the round fish will bite him and cause him such distress that he may give up the whole idea."

Unconvinced, the woman thanked him and resumed her loud complaints.

An egg seller stopped, shouting "Eggs! Reputable eggs to sell!" He asked what was the matter. When he was told, he scratched his head in some perplexity. He was quite plainly giving the matter a great deal of thought. At last he said, "Here, take these few eggs. Put them in the ashes of your fire. If the Nung-guama is bitten by snakes and by fish, his fingers will bleed. Then he will want to put them in the ashes to stop the bleeding. If he does, the eggs will burst in his face. That should startle him out of his wickedness."

The woman was past comfort, but she took the eggs and resumed her wails louder than ever.

This brought up to her a seller of millstones. "I will give you this millstone," he told her. "It weighs more than forty katties.

Hang it onto the beam above your bed. If the Nung-guama should dart beneath it, you may cut the string, and perhaps the millstone will crush the beast's head. But then," he said, "it may be necessary to finish him off, so here is an iron bar with which you might beat out any life that is left in him."

By this time the evening was coming on. The woman had to abandon her journey to her parents. So, to ease her sorrow, she ate the cakes, and then hired a porter to carry all her gifts back to her own house.

She felt sure her end was near, but clutching at what hope there was, she set out all the presents exactly as she had been advised to do.

By that time it was dark. She went to bed and lay waiting, quaking with fear.

Nothing happened. The watchman passed by, calling out the second watch of the night, and then again, tapping his wooden drum *tap, tap-tap* for the third watch, calling, "Beware robbers. Here I come," in his old, quavering voice.

Nothing happened. All was still.

Until . . . *Flup: flup—flup: flup*. It was the Nung-guama's soft and flappish feet outside the door. "Heh! Heh!"

"Open the door," growled the Nung-guama softly, "I want to scrunch you up."

The woman could not stir for fear.

With a fearful rush, the beast beat the door down. He howled with rage as the needles tore and the dung dirtied his hands. "What's this?" he raged. "All prickles and dirt here! But now I'm in, I'll finish her off. Ah! First here's some water to wash my fingers. *A-a-h!*" (as the snakes jabbed with poisoned fangs at his hands). "What a place is this! Ah! The very thing. This cooking pot will have good, hot water to ease this pain. O-oh!" (as the round fish bit at his fingers). "I must be bleeding to death in the dark here. I'll stanch the blood in the ashes in the hearth. *E-eu!*" (as the eggs popped in his face and filled his eyes with hot shell). "I'm bleeding to death! I can't see! I'll

scrunch the old woman up for this. Where are you, you hag?" And he went, groping and flopping—*Flup-Flup*—across the room to the bed.

At the right moment the widow cut the string. Down fell the millstone, crash onto the Nung-guama's head. He collapsed as if he were dead. No doubt he was. But to make quite sure, the now comforted widow gave him a few heavy bangs with the iron bar.

And so, instead of being eaten by a vulgar creature with the manners of a barbarian, the widow found herself safe and whole.

And as for the mess and damage caused by the Nung-guama, well, the sale of his carcass provided enough cash to put everything to rights, and still left a little over.

How the Ox Came Upon Earth

I N China now, as for many thousands of years, it is the ox that pulls the plow and does all the heavy work about the farm.

But in very ancient times there was no such animal as the ox upon Earth. There was only, twinkling high up in the Heavens, the Ox Star.

And in those times men found it very hard indeed to live. Work as hard as they might, pinch and scrape as they had to, they were lucky if they were able to eat as often as, say, once every five or once every six days.

The Emperor of Heaven looked down on this very sorry state of things and was heartily grieved for the plight of the people on Earth. Yet he felt sure that men could do better than this for themselves. He thought he would see what effect a little encouragement would have.

So he sent the Ox Star down to Earth as his messenger.

"Tell the people," said the Emperor of Heaven, "that if they are truly energetic, there is no reason why they should not eat at least once in three days."

Now the Ox, who was not very intelligent, felt very proud and excited about this errand. He had never before been used in this grand way, as a messenger of the Heavenly Emperor.

He went lumbering down to Earth as quickly as he could, and gathered the people of the earth together to hear his message.

"I am to tell you," he bellowed, "from the Emperor of Heaven himself, that if you are truly energetic, you may have three meals every day."

You can imagine how warmly this announcement was cheered by the hungry people.

When the Ox returned to Heaven, the Emperor was very vexed.

"Stupid creature," he said, "I told you to tell the people of Earth that if they worked they might eat once in three days. Now you have told them that they can eat three times a day. How can such a thing be? Men are but small creatures and weakly. How can they grow sufficient to provide such great quantities of food? Yet I must keep my word. You must go down yourself, and with your brute strength help these poor creatures to plow. With your work, they will be able to eat three times every day."

And so the Ox was sent down to Earth to help man to grow his food, and ever since then, with oxen to plow for him, man has been able to eat three times every day.

General Chu-Ki Liang

THERE are no fairies or magic in this story, except in the way that there are fairies and magic in every tale. But it is quite true, just as if there really were fairies in it. And it all happened sometime about the year 200 A.D.

At this time the kingdom of Shu was being invaded by a very powerful army.

Two armies of the kingdom of Shu were far away in the south, doing battle with other enemies. So General Ma took all the soldiers who remained and went out to oppose the invaders.

Unfortunately, he allowed himself and his army to get entangled in wild mountain country, and in his confusion he sought refuge with his men on the top of a mountain. Beseiged there by the enemy army, he decided upon a wild attack to get out of his difficulties, but the attack failed, General Ma was killed, and his army was scattered.

This sad defeat left the important city of Chieh-ting of the Shu kingdom completely unguarded, and the invading General Szu-ma, with his huge army, set forth gleefully to capture it.

What was to be done?

In the city of Chieh-ting there was an old general, but he had no army. Those troops of the kingdom of Shu, who had been fighting far away in the south, were now marching back toward the city as fast as they could. But they were too far away to arrive in time to defeat Szu-ma's army, which was now only a day's march from the undefended city.

And so, on a still morning of summer hotness, frightened citizens looking out from the city wall could see, far away down the white road over the plain, the glint of armor as Szu-ma's fearful army came into sight.

Slowly onward that army came, company by company, spearmen, archers, men with stabbing knives, and those with thick swords. Captains, gaily plumed, galloped back and forth.

At last the leading company came within plain sight of the city gates. At a shout from their captain, the soldiers halted. The captain rode rapidly back down the column, to seek General Szu-ma.

After awhile the general and his chief officers rode jingling up to the leading troops. The general's face darkened as he looked long at the entrance to the city. What he saw was the city gate, wide open. Four old soldiers (all that had been left in the city) were sweeping the road along which General Szu-ma wished to pass, as if in official welcome. And over the gate itself sat the old General Chu-Ki Liang. He was playing a friendly tune upon a moon guitar, and paused from time to time to refresh himself with a cup of wine which he waved in a welcoming manner.

General Szu-ma opened his great mouth and shouted loudly, "You may be clever, but I am not to be caught in such a simple trap." Then, telling his captains that without doubt a large army was in hiding behind the city walls, he ordered his army to retreat.

From on top of the city gate, General Chu-Ki Liang watched the enemy as it slowly withdrew across the plain. He did not for a moment stop playing his moon guitar, unless it was to refresh himself with a sip from his cup of wine.

It was not until the enemy was almost out of sight that General Chu-Ki Liang permitted himself to smile a little. By that time, the four old soldiers, leaning on their brooms, were laughing aloud.

A Tongue of Gold and Words of Jade

I N the temple there were, of course, many gods. There
were hundreds of them; gods of pestilence and of fire, of
food, of motherhood, of war. There were, in fact, gods of
almost everything you could wish for, and gods of most of the
things you would not like at all.

They all stood in hall after hall on stone platforms. Some
were huge, their painted faces almost lost in the roof shadows.
Others were of middle height, and some were quite small. There
they were, smiling, laughing, grinning, scowling or gnashing
sharp teeth. And at their feet were the burning or spent candles
of those who had come to ask big favors or to pray that evil be
arrested.

One of the most wearying tasks for the monks who kept the
temple was sweeping the temple clean. This had to be done every
day. It was not just a matter of sweeping the open floor. The
tops of the platforms upon which the gods stood had also to be
swept. And what an awkward task that was, because the great
feet of the gods were in the way, and one had to sweep carefully
around them.

A duty so irritating was naturally always given to the youngest
and newest monk. And in this temple, at the time of which I am
speaking, this was a young man named Chu Yuan-chang.

When he had been doing this work for some weeks, the other
monks noticed that he always finished it much sooner than
anyone had ever done, and that the temple was always far
cleaner that it had ever been before.

After they had talked about this for a long time, the monks

determined to find out how the youth managed this matter so well. So some of them hid and watched.

They saw Chu Yuan-chang come into the first hall with his broom. Before he began to sweep the floor, he said to the gods. "Now then, come down, all of you!" And the gods, some of them grumbling in a good-humored way, all climbed down stiffly from their platforms, so that Chu was free to sweep cleanly there. Then, when he had cleaned all the platforms with a few swift strokes of his broom, Chu said, "Come on now. Get back out of my way," and forthwith the gods, great and small, clambered back, groaning with stiff joints, onto their pedestals. Then Chu quickly swept the floor.

The monks came out from hiding and did reverence to Chu Yuan-chang, for they knew that he must have a tongue of gold and words of jade, which—as has been said of old—can move the gods. They had no doubt that he was destined for future greatness. And they were right, because before he died, Chu Yuan-chang became Emperor.

Why the Cock Eats Worms

IN very olden days the cock used to have horns, just like dragons have. He was a brave sight, strutting grandly in the dust outside the farm gate, with his blue-black sickle feathers, his bright red comb and his proud horns.

One day a dragon came to see him. He came sailing majestically across the sky. He was quite big. When he flew through a cloud, his head came out of one end of it while his tail was still sticking out of the other. This dragon was mostly green, but the edges of each green scale on his hide glowed red.

He settled quite gently on the earth, with his head and forefeet near to the cock. Where his tail was, who can tell? It was a long, long way away. Fire no longer came out of his nostrils. Just a faint wisp of smoke drifted up from each of them and whirled off sideways in the brisk, spring breeze.

"Honorable cock," said the dragon, in a lazy, rumbling kind of voice. "How is it with you, well or bad?"

"It is good, noble dragon," replied the cock, squinting sideways at a speck of something eatable in the dust.

"That is good," sighed the dragon, and he blew steam thoughtfully into the sparkling air.

"May I enquire the state of your health and fortune?" asked the cock, not to be outdone in politeness.

"Good. Good," said the dragon.

"Good," said the cock.

Then there was a rather long silence while the dragon pondered just how he could best explain why he had come visiting, and the cock wondered for what purpose the dragon was being so affable.

At last the dragon had to speak. "Friend cock," he said, "I have a great wish to visit the Heavenly Regions, and to pay my respects to the Great Heavenly Ones—"

"That is a good thought."

"But, alas!" sighed the dragon, "I have no horns."

The cock looked at him carefully. Yes, it was so. The dragon had no horns. "But how does this affect matters?" the cock enquired.

"Without horns, how can I visit the Heavenly Regions?" exclaimed the dragon fretfully. "I would be mocked and laughed at."

The cock clucked sympathetically.

"Now, if only you would lend me your horns," said the dragon slowly, looking at the cock carefully, with one eye.

The cock pecked uneasily at the ground for awhile. "How would I be sure that I would get them back again?" he asked sternly.

"I have thought of that," said the dragon. "The worm is well known to you. He will speak for me. Let us ask him. He will assure you that I will return your beautiful horns."

So they both tapped on the earth, and very soon the worm appeared. He spoke most strongly of the dragon's honesty and good faith. "The dragon is sure to give your horns back to you," he said.

The cock thought that this should be safe enough. And he rather liked the idea of the dragon going up to the Heavenly Regions. When he came back, the cock would ask him what it was like up there. It might be nice to go there himself one day.

So the cock gave his horns to the dragon, and the dragon spread his wings. With a rush of hot air, he was borne up into the deep sky. Cock and worm watched his going, with wistful interest.

Next morning, almost before it was light, the cock mounted upon a dungheap, and throwing back his head, called loudly, "Give me back my horns! Give me back my horns." There was

no answer. The last stars fled away to the west, leaving a great, empty sky.

When it was noon and the dragon had not yet returned, the cock went to the worm. "Never fear," the worm reassured him. "The dragon is sure to bring back your horns. If not today, well, certainly tomorrow."

But although every morning the cock crowed loudly, "Give me back my horns!" he never saw that dragon again.

When at last hope had died and hot anger had taken its place, the cock sought out the worm and ate him up. And he gave orders to all his children that forever more they were to eat every worm that they could find. It was right, the cock explained, that the worms should suffer for having deceived him out of his horns. And besides, he had discovered that worms are very nice to eat.

Ever since then cocks have had no horns, and worms have had no peace.

The Two Fools

A VILLAGER named Lin came into possession of ten pieces of silver. Never before in his life had he seen so much money in his own hands. He was full of fear that this treasure might be stolen from him. Where could he hide it? He looked around his bare hut. He could see no safe hiding place, except for the wall. Feverishly, stopping a hundred times to run to the door and peer out for fear of someone seeing what he was at, he scratched a hole in the mud wall. Into it he tucked the silver. Then he covered the hole with fresh mud. And he would not let anyone into his hut until the fresh mud had dried and the patch in the wall had ceased to show.

But even then he was ill at ease. Suppose someone were to look in the hut for the treasure? Where would they look for it? Where could they look? There was nowhere money might be hidden, except in the wall. His face sweated with alarm at this thought. Then an idea came to him. He borrowed a brush and some ink, and on the wall where he had hidden his money he wrote: THERE IS NO MONEY HIDDEN IN THIS WALL.

Days later, another villager (Wan was his name) came into the hut to look for him. Lin was not there. Looking around him, Wan saw the writing on the wall. "There is no money hidden in this wall," read Wan slowly. His face puckered with puzzlement. Now, why should Neighbor Lin write such a foolish thing? he thought. Of course there's no money hidden in the wall. But wait. Why say so? Unless, perhaps, there is. And in a moment Wan was tearing at the wall with his nails.

He soon found the money. How delighted this rogue was with his cleverness! Then fear came. Suppose anyone should

115

think that it was he who had stolen Lin's money? He would be dragged before the magistrate, beaten until he confessed, and then. . . . He could not bear to think any further. No one must suspect that he had robbed Lin. But how could he stop anyone from doing that? His foolish face broke into a grin of relief. Of course. Why hadn't he thought of it before?

He, too, borrowed ink and brush, and on the pillar of his own door he wrote, with anxious care: I, WAN, AM AN HONEST MAN. I DID NOT STEAL LIN'S MONEY FROM OUT OF THE HOLE IN THE WALL.

The Hungry Serpent

INSIDE the walls of a city now long since crumbled into yellow dust there was a lotus lake near to a great temple.

It was a breath-taking sight in the early summer days. The temple roof, down-sweeping and up-curving, was covered with tiles of brightest blue, and down the roof ridges figures of dragons and lions and tigers and green porcelain kings sported together. This pure blue and these grass-green figures were reflected in the lake's still waters between patches of blood-red lotus flowers.

The people came from far away to see the lotus lake with its red blossoms and its reflections of blue and green.

One clump of flowers in the lake was specially worthy of notice. It was far bigger and redder than the others. It stuck out high above the water, instead of lying meekly upon the surface like the other lotus flowers. Also, although it always stood up out of the water in the morning, it always sank down under the surface when evening came. People used to put things upon it for the pleasure, at evening, of seeing them drawn down into the lake when the light of day began to fade.

Do you know, it was not long before people began to talk about that strange blood-red lotus cluster? A monk was heard to say that it was a lotus throne such as belong to the Buddhas of the Three Ages. And then it was no time at all before it was believed to have some connection with the Western Paradise. And from that it was argued that any virtuous person who sat upon that seat would go straight to Paradise.

In China, it is a gracious and good thing to be old. Respect and deference are paid to age, and an aged person may decide, one day or another, that it is now a fitting and convenient time to die and go to Paradise. Because of this, as those stories about the lotus lake spread around the city, old persons began to try this method of securing the bliss of Heaven. The method seemed to work very well. An ancient person would be placed comfortably upon the scarlet flowers, and then at evening would be received into the lake's black waters as the flower clump lowered itself under the surface. No body, no spirit came back with any unfavorable reports, and so this process soon became the accepted method of leaving life on earth in that city.

The years went by. No one can tell how many old people left this world by way of the lotus throne.

The district governor's mother was by this time sixty years old. The thought came to her that it was time to leave this earth. She sent for her son. He came before her, bowing low, to ask what was her desire. She said:

"Son, I am a great lady, the mother of a high official, but I am only a woman, as other women are. All women, as they reach a great age, go to Paradise by way of the lotus throne. It is in my mind, now that I, too, am old, to reach Paradise by the same way. Do you therefore make preparations for my going tomorrow, for I have no desire to see any more of this world. You have been a dutiful son and have won high position. Be virtuous in life, so as to deserve bliss afterward. And I shall hope to see you persevering on earth as I look out upon you from the Western Paradise."

The District Governor was very shocked at those words. He did not know of these happenings in the lotus lake. When he was told what the people believed about it, he was very vexed.

He went back to his mother and bowed again. "Madam," he said, "you must not believe such silly tales. You must live and give me the pleasure of maintaining you for many years yet. In fact, I will not hear of your dying now and in this vulgar manner."

The great lady was very shocked. "Undutiful Son!" she ex-

claimed. "How can you hope to govern when you do not even know how to obey your mother? And where is your sense of virtue? All good sons rejoice when their parents attain to Paradise. What right have you to keep me from it any longer?"

The son bowed again. "Your pardon, Mother. It shall be as you wish. I will go instantly and prepare food and clothing for your journey to Heaven."

The mother stopped him. "In Paradise," she reminded him, "there is plenty of food and clothing and everything that is necessary. There is no need for any preparation. I will take only some incense and a staff. Please order the litter to be ready to carry me to the lotus lake tomorrow morning."

The District Governor went away very troubled in his mind. He did not believe that what the people thought about the lotus flower could be true. After much thought, he decided on a plan.

He summoned his steward. He told him to set servants to filling sacks with gunpowder and with quicklime. When the steward asked, "How many sacks?" the District Governor told him, "Very many. Load all the gunpowder and quicklime that we have."

When these sacks were ready, they were loaded upon a boat, and that very evening the boat was rowed out onto the lake to where the lotus flower still stood erect above the water.

The District Governor, standing up in the prow of the boat, ordered a sack of gunpowder to be poured into the flower. The servants heaved it in. It disappeared. Then a sack of quicklime. That, too, was sucked down into the flower. Then a sack of gunpowder again. How long this went on, it would be hard to tell. And it would be difficult to say how many sacks were finally poured into the lotus. If I said one hundred, it would not be enough, though if I said two hundred, that might be too many.

Be that as it may, the last sack was tipped into the lotus. The servants stood still, wiping sweat from their brows. The great blood-red lotus reared its head into the air, as if waiting for more, and then sank noiselessly under the water.

Trembling a little, the District Governor was rowed back to the shore. It was a bold thing to do, to send a whole boatload of gunpowder and quicklime to the Western Paradise.

Very early the next morning the District Governor arrived at his mother's house with his sons and his daughters and all his relatives, ready to escort the old lady to the Western Paradise. But when they arrived at the lake, their procession could not get near to it at first, so great was the crowd of people.

Excited men reported to the District Governor: "There is a great serpent in the lake."

When the District Governor's men had beaten a way to the lakeside clear for him, he could plainly see that there was indeed a great serpent. All that was visible of it was enormous, and no one could tell how much more of it there might be, so twisted and convulsed it was, as if it had suffered some mighty pain in the stomach.

The District Governor ordered men to cut the creature open. They cut and cut. It was so big a serpent that they cut for three days. Then at last they had it laid open. It was obvious now that the blood-red lotus flower had been in fact no flower at all, but the serpent's tongue. And what had happened to all the poor old people who had lain upon it? Inside the serpent, countless buttons and piles of bones told the sad story. All those amiable old people had been digested—everything, except the gunpowder and the quicklime, which was still smoking in the morning air.

Simple Wang

Now I must tell you of Simple Wang. He once lived in a village whose name is no longer even remembered. Only a rough path led to this village, and it led no farther. So no travelers passed through, no caravans of merchants, no cavalcades of officials. The villagers lived in an insignificant way, cut off from the benefits of refined conversation.

They were a simple people, but among them Wang was renowned for being simple to the point of stupidity.

Very early one summer morning, when the scent of the gwehwa tree sweetened the dewy air, he stood manfully outside his modest home, about to make a journey to the city. He had already shouldered his long carrying pole, and from it, before him and behind, hung wide bamboo baskets stacked high with charcoal. He had never before been to the city, or for that matter anywhere else. His wife had urged him to undertake this adventure. She hoped that a fine profit might be made from selling charcoal to prudent citizens who had the coming winter's bleakness in mind.

Wang, with a desperate heave, took up the weight of his load and set off briskly, with the little tripping steps of those who carry great burdens. For a short way his young wife ran beside him. "Go safely," she begged. "Return prosperous, and bring me back a present."

She was very pretty. So Wang, grunting a little under his load, asked what he should bring.

"A new comb," cried the little, twinkling wife.

"A comb?" said Wang, not being able to think in a moment,

full as he was of importance and excitement, exactly what a comb was.

The combs they used in those times were of wood and were curved. His wife pointed with a long finger to the crescent moon which still showed palely in the morning sky. "Like that," she told him, and then, ashamed at having run so far along the public street in daylight, dropped behind and left Wang to pursue his journey.

He, having looked dully at the moon for some time so as to impress it on his mind, now made great haste away from his home toward the unknown city.

On his way, you may be sure, he both saw and heard things too strange to be imagined. That is not so remarkable as the fact that he did arrive safely at the city gates and did after a few days sell all his charcoal at a good price.

In the early evening, relieved of his burden and made bold by the possession of a weighty string of cash, he wandered in the jostling city street, where banners of red and yellow, blue and green, hung from shop fronts and balconies, and where the frantic hubbub of clamoring shopmen and shouting buyers made everyone smile with happiness.

Suddenly, out of nowhere, Wang remembered his wife's present. He stood stock still, while hurrying people pushed round him, jolted against him, and all but trod over him. Wang did not even notice them. Now, what did I say I would buy? he was anxiously asking himself. He had not the least idea what it was—until he remembered the moon. With a chuckle of relief, he looked upward to where a thin strip of sky could be seen between the close-leaning shop roofs. Looking down toward the street's end, he saw the moon. It was full now and hung low and white in the evening light.

"Something round," thought Wang, a little bewildered. The idea of roundness did not suggest anything to him. Scratching his head in perplexity, he edged along by the open shops. Almost at once he saw what he wanted. It was quite round. It could not be any rounder, thought Wang, almost hugging himself with satisfaction.

So without haggling over the price and without inspecting his purchase, he paid what was asked, and wrapping it in a piece of cotton cloth, hurried off, with only a casual bow to the shopkeeper.

What Wang had bought was a mirror. He did not even know what a mirror was. No person in his village had ever owned one or seen one; nor had any of them heard of such a thing.

The same favorable spirits who had protected Wang in his going must also have presided over his homecoming, for he reached his own village after a journey of many days, unhurt, unplundered, and still clutching the gift for his wife.

Alone with her, he produced the present. Trembling with excitement, the little wife seized the parcel and opened it. Her cry of dismay when she perceived that this was not a comb changed to lamentation when, looking into the mirror, she saw her own pretty face.

"*Ayee-ah!*" she wailed. "My husband has brought back a beautiful new wife." (For I must tell you that in these parts at this time a man might have more than one wife.)

The poor girl's unhappiness was extreme. Crying and complaining, she ran off to the house of her father, which, happily, was but a short distance down the street.

There she flung herself at her mother's feet.

"My husband has brought home a new wife," she wailed, handing her mother the mirror.

The mother took up the strange thing with great caution. Then, looking in it, she saw her own face.

"Well, Daughter," she said, "if your honorable husband had to bring home a second wife, he need not, surely, have chosen an ugly old hag like this one."

Who can tell where this sad misunderstanding might have led them all, had not it been decided to take the strange matter to the village magistrate?

He, as simple as any of them, took up the mirror. He looked at it. How could he know that it was his own image that he saw there? He thought at once that some waggish person had dressed up to look like him.

"Impertinent creature!" he said with cold anger. "With what shameless freedom do you show your contempt for the law when in coming before me you make a mock of my appearance?"

And he ordered them all—Wang, the pretty wife, and mother-in-law—to be whipped.

That was bad. But while they all three resisted this punishment with great strugglings and loud lamentations, the mirror was broken.

And that was good, wasn't it?

Chu and the King of the Underworld

THIS is a story about Chu, who was a rogue and a trickster. One day as he sat idle in his miserable hut the bright sun cast a beam through a crack in the crazy wall.

Chu shook his head irritably. He went slowly outside and looked up into the sky. "Sunshine P'usa!" he shouted angrily. "What right have you to come into my house when I have not asked you to call? I am very angry. I shall complain to the Jade Emperor of Heaven."

At this the sun was very frightened.

"Oh! Do not do that, honorable sir," he pleaded. "See, there is a pot of silver just in front of your fine house there. Take that, I beg, and be satisfied."

Chu looked, and there it was, just in front of his house, a pot brimming with silver. He took it up quickly and hid it safely indoors.

That very night the moon shone full. Chu, wakeful and thinking with some glee about his fine silver, found himself annoyed by a shaft of moonlight which came in through the open doorway. He lost no time in getting up and running eagerly outside. "Moonlight P'usa!" he bawled at the yellow moon. "How dare you enter my house when you have not been invited? My heart is full of bitterness because of this. I shall complain to the Jade Emperor of Heaven."

The quiet moon was scared. "Please do no such thing," she begged. "Do have the goodness to take the pot of gold which lies just behind your splendid house, and think no more of the matter."

Chu, running quickly around to the back of his hut, found the pot of gold, and hugging it tenderly, went indoors happily.

These fortunate happenings may have made Chu proud. Otherwise, how can I explain his conduct? Only a few days later he went, as is prudent, to make devotion at the Temple of the Plague Gods. But instead of behaving in a devout manner, as is polite, he began to storm and shout.

"What a lot of old Gods you are!" he scolded. "Jumbled up anyhow in twos and threes. Dusty and dirty too. What bad Gods you must be! I shall complain to the Jade Emperor of Heaven about you."

Then, with an expecting smile on his face, he waited for some reward.

But these terrible Plague Gods were more used to being feared than being frightened. Chu stared up at their great, snarling faces, high up in the gloom of the ceiling, until the smile on his face became fixed into a grin of alarm. No answer came. Chu turned and ran, stumbling, from the temple.

As soon as he was gone the Plague Gods made a complaint to their master. He was Yen-lo-Wang, the King of the Underworld.

This great king was extremely angry. He at once sent the Bee Spirit to fetch Chu down to the Underworld for judgment.

Chu, as he ran in the cheerful sunlight, recovered his courage. When he got home, he sat very alert in case trouble should follow this quarrel with the Plague Gods.

And so he spied the Bee Spirit, hovering and buzzing on its way to seize him. With not a moment to spare, Chu pasted paper over every hole and crack in his hut, except for one small hole. Over this, on the inside, he fixed a pig's bladder.

The Bee Spirit arrived at the hut. "*B-zzz*," at one hole. "Can't get in—*B-zzz*," at another hole. "Can't get in—*B-zzz*—Ah! This is it! Where am I? Trapped!"

When Yen-lo-Wang, the King of the Underworld, found that his Bee Spirit had not returned, he was even more angry. He sent another messenger, more desperate in its ways, the One-legged Spirit.

This one was also seen by the watchful Chu. As quickly as he could, Chu gathered up armfuls of prickly thorns and filled his hut with them. Then he sat down in the middle of them.

The One-legged Spirit peeped in at the door and saw Chu, sitting quietly with a smile of hospitality on his face. So he dashed in with a fierce cry, but once in he could neither attack nor retreat for the pain of the prickles. So Chu tied him up and laid him in a corner just below where the Bee Spirit still buzzed inside the pig's bladder.

The King of the Underworld waited in vain for the return of the One-legged Spirit and his prisoner. Then, his face calm with rage, he mounted his Thousand-League Horse and went himself to deal with this fellow. With him he took the two most dreaded messengers of the Underworld, Ox-Head and Horse-Face. As everybody knew, there was no resisting their summons.

As before, Chu knew of their coming. He sent his wife to greet them. With a welcoming smile and with profuse bowings, she invited them to dine.

When the meal was finished and polite conversation was ended, Chu went to the stable and took out the old water buffalo on which he would ride back to the Underworld with his captors. Yen-lo-Wang mounted his Thousand-League Horse. Chu clambered unsteadily onto the water buffalo. As they departed, Chu's wife hung two burning arrows onto the water buffalo's tail, as she had been told to do.

Terrified by the pain, the water buffalo plunged off at such a pace that even the famous Thousand-League Horse of Yen-lo-Wang could not keep up with it.

When the arrows fell off, the water buffalo stopped, and the King of the Underworld was able to overtake Chu.

"What an amazing animal!" he cried to Chu. "What kind of a water buffalo is this that can outpace the fastest horse in all the world?"

"It is a Thousand-League Water Buffalo," said Chu, with a sly smile.

"May I try it?" the King asked eagerly.

"Alas!" said Chu. "It will only run if I ride it. For anyone else it will merely walk."

"Surely there could be some arrangement . . . ?" the King of the Underworld began.

Chu pretended to ponder. "I wonder . . ." he said. "If you were to put on my clothes, I do not think this stupid beast would notice the deception."

The King was all agog. The change of clothes was soon made. Chu, in resplendent silk, sat upon the Thousand-League Horse. The King, in faded rags, bestrode the Thousand-League Water Buffalo.

The King gave the water buffalo a brisk cut with his whip, and the heavy animal stood as still as stone. Chu did but lightly press with his heels, and the Thousand-League Horse sped, like a shooting star, down to the Underworld.

There, in the royal robes, Chu seated himself on the throne. He said to the servant ghosts, "Chu, the rogue, is following me on a water buffalo. When he arrives, give him a good beating."

So when, much later, heated and tired with belaboring the water buffalo, the true king arrived, he was promptly pulled off the beast by the servant ghosts and beaten energetically. Indeed it was only the arrival of Ox-Head and Horse-Face that saved him from more prolonged punishment.

Chu laughed heartily when the King of the Underworld, bruised and smarting, confronted him. And he was quite disappointed when the King refused to regard the matter as a merry jest. Far from smiling, the King ordered that Chu should be boiled in oil.

The little spirits bore Chu off to hold him safely while the caldron was being heated.

Chu had been thinking hard.

"Do you not want to become rich?" he asked the little spirits

as they poured more and more oil into the caldron.

They all wanted to become rich, and asked him earnestly how this could be managed.

"Nothing simpler," said Chu. "The King of the Underworld must be very ignorant to think that all this oil is needed to boil just one small man. Why don't you put just enough in the caldron to roast me gently—and sell all the rest? Then you will be rich."

The little spirits were delighted with this plan, and at once did just what Chu had said.

Then, when the oil was bubbling, Chu was put into the caldron with gentleness and with regret; they would have preferred to roast someone whose conversation was less agreeable.

However, since there was so little oil in the caldron, Chu was able to keep out of the hissing mess by pressing his feet against one side and his shoulders against the other.

In vain the King of the Underworld stoked the fire. The uncooked Chu still entertained him and the little spirits with animated conversation.

In despair, the King had him taken out, and ordered the little spirits to drag him to the banks of the Yen Yang, the river of Hell, and to leave him there to freeze to death.

Left there, Chu tried to sing cheering songs to himself, but when the keen cold seized him he began to shout and bellow. A carp stuck his head out of the water and looked at him sympathetically.

"Please tell me," begged Chu, "how can I get across this river to the Upper World?"

"Quite simple," said the carp. "I will carry you on my back." And he did.

And Chu walked away into the world again, a free man.

Was he happy because of his marvelous escape? It must be confessed that he was vexed with himself as he hurried home. Why had he not thought of catching that carp? he was asking himself. He could have sold it to buy wine.

A San and the Wang Liang

To be bold and resolute is good. But without honesty, no man can prosper for long.

Let me tell you the story of A San, who was bold and resolute also—but who was not honest—and of the Wang Liang.

As every child in China knows, the Wang Liang are very big and are covered with long hair. They walk upon two feet, like ordinary people, and indeed can mix with folk without being noticed very much, so long as they cover themselves up well with plenty of clothing. But they are very rarely seen, for they like to live high up in the great snow mountains where the air is thin and cold. In these regions, if they meet a man, they eat him up as fast as they can.

So of course these are very dangerous creatures, unless you know how to deal with them; then it is quite simple to master them. If you meet a Wang Liang when you are away up high in the great snow mountains, you must take a stick, which must be pointed at one end, and press the blunt end against your breast, pointing the sharp end toward the Wang Liang. This at once gives the Wang Liang a feeling of great uneasiness; he is so upset that you can make him do anything you wish before you let him go.

A San, a young carpenter, must have known of this trick. One evening as he was descending the mountains on his way home from some work he had been doing in the valley village over on the other side, he met a Wang Liang face to face. It must have been seven feet high. Its face was scowling; its teeth grated together. Long gray hair covered its body. It looked very hungry.

But A San did not shriek or run away. He very bravely seized a sharpened bamboo pole, and placing the blunt end against his breast, pointed the sharp end toward this beastly creature.

The Wang Liang at once stopped grinding his teeth and licking his lips, and began to look quite frightened.

"Let me go! Let me go!" begged the Wang Liang, trying hard to look as friendly as possible.

A San did not let the bamboo pole move even by so much as an inch.

"Let me go!" again whined the Wang Liang. "My wife and my poor six children will be waiting for something to eat."

This remark did not please A San, who knew very well just what sort of meat this horrid family would have liked to dine upon. He pointed the pole more directly toward the Wang Liang and said, "I will not let you move from this spot until you have given me a present!"

The Wang Liang nodded his ugly head in agreement, and bending down, tugged off his boot and offered it to A San.

Now, this is another thing to remember about Wang Liang. Never accept a boot for a present, for the boot is really a coffin. Clever A San knew this, and very sternly refused the boot.

"I want that straw cap you have on your head," he said firmly.

At this the Wang Liang began to curse and complain, for the straw cap was very valuable magic. Worn by a human person, it would make him quite invisible.

However, seeing that A San would not change his mind, the Wang Liang very unwillingly took off his cap and gave it to the young fellow. Then A San, still pointing the pole at the Wang Liang, moved cautiously around him, and then backed away, step by step, until he was out of danger. Then, with the straw cap under his arm, he ran. But he need not have done so. Wang Liang are so upset by this treatment that they are almost harmless for hours afterward.

A San hastened home with his straw cap, his mind busy with

all the exciting uses to which he could put it. It was too dark by
now for him to test its powers, but when the reached the door
of his own hut he put it on his head.

In the one room his wife was busy cooking by the light of a
large oil lamp, for she had expected her master to return late at
night. A San walked in, and his wife started at the noise of his
footsteps, but seeing no one, shook her head doubtfully and
turned to her cooking again. A San could not help laughing
loudly at her puzzlement. This only confounded the poor wife
more, because she heard her husband's laughter but could not
see him.

This satisfied A San that the cap did truly make him invisible.
He took it off, and told his wife all that had happened.

Now A San could have enjoyed many fine jokes with his
magic cap, and might, too, have done much good with its aid.
But, unhappily, his thoughts turned toward using it to steal
things.

The first time he tried he was unlucky. Putting it on his head, he went to steal oranges from a fruit stall in the street. Oddly enough, there happened to be a Wang Liang there in the crowd, dressed as an ordinary man. When the Wang Liang noticed the magic cap and saw what A San was doing, he quickly knocked the cap off the young thief's head. While A San groped to pick it up again, he was of course discovered.

What an outcry there was when A San was seen in broad daylight to be stealing oranges from his neighbor's fruit stall! A San received much abuse and a very heavy beating from the fruit-stall man, who was a big fellow and a little inclined to bad temper.

This piece of ill-fortune did not make A San repent of his evil ways, but it did make him more cautious. Certainly he did not himself venture on the next escapade with the magic cap. He sent his wife instead. He ordered her to go into the house of a rich man, to steal silver. All went well at first. His wife put on the magic cap and walked quietly in, past the gatehouse keeper, who was sitting in the gateway, thoughtfully smoking a long pipe. She went through the doorway of the house, and although the rich man came right past her, no one could see her. The silver was in the bedchamber of the rich man's daughter, who, because the afternoon was so hot, was asleep there. Just as the wife was about to snatch up the silver, the maiden coughed in her sleep. Quite forgetting that she was invisible, the wife, thinking she was discovered, ran screaming out of the house in fright. For many years afterward in that home the family would tell the story of the spirit which had run screaming through the house on a hot afternoon in the month of great heat, its feet pattering on the floors.

A San could see that he would have to manage things for himself. He began to wear the cap, and to steal silver and precious things from the houses of rich people. So successful was he that it was not long before he himself became rich also. With all his wealth, however, he was careful always to dress in poor clothes, so that suspicion might not fall upon him. The only relaxation he allowed himself was gambling, of which he was greatly fond.

It seemed likely that he would live long to enjoy the wealth he had so wickedly gained. It is true that one morning his wife, who was nearsighted, was just about to light the fire with the magic cap, thinking it to be a bundle of rice straw. It was only by lucky chance that A San saw her mistake in time to prevent it. What a great smack he gave her! For, too often, riches and idleness promote shortness of temper.

A San might very well have taken this incident as a warning that good things do not last forever, but he did not. He went on stealing and gambling as industriously as before. And the more he gambled, the more he was forced to steal, because when he gambled he nearly always lost his silver.

One night when he was gambling with some strangers, with more recklessness even than usual, he found that all his money was gone. These others who played with him looked at him queerly, ready to mock at him if he should have to stop playing and meekly go home.

When he threw an old straw cap on the table, they laughed at once.

"What is this filthy thing?"

"How much are we to wager against this piece of rubbish?"

"If that is all you have to bet with, pray do not waste our time any longer." These were the sort of remarks that were made to him.

A San flushed until his yellow face was the color of copper.

"Do not despise this thing," he shouted imprudently. "It is of great value. Anyone who wears this cap is invisible."

At this the strangers laughed more loudly until one of them, in sport, put it on his head. The others stared, gaping, at the place where he had been sitting. Without doubt, he had become invisible.

The next thing that happened was that an invisible hand

quickly gathered up all the money that was lying on the gambling table; then everything else that was valuable was picked up as well. Invisible feet could be heard running away down the street, and a mocking laugh came from the thieving stranger as he made off with all their possessions and with the magic cap of A San.

The Dark Maiden from the
Ninth Heaven

THERE was once a poor young man who lived in a broken-down kiln that nobody used any more. When anyone would give him work, he did it well, and so could eat for awhile. But since the great drought things had been bad in that province; often the best that poor Hwang could do for himself was to collect firewood or dung and hope to sell them.

New Year's Day is a great festival. On New Year's Eve all debts must be paid, and on New Year's Day itself there is feasting and rejoicing, and people are careful to think propitious thoughts, for what is done and thought about on that day affects the whole of the year to come.

On New Year's Eve, then, Hwang collected the little money that was owing to him, and added it to the small store he had laid by. Then next morning he went away into the town, to buy some fine food for his own lonely celebrations.

On his way he stopped at a field of beautiful fresh cabbages, and cut one for himself, for on that happy season anyone could help himself from any farmer's field. Hwang went on, with the cabbage under his arm, wishing good luck and long life to the farmer who had grown it. Too many farmers poured manure over their cabbages just before the New Year, so that passers-by would not come to gather them.

As Hwang drew near the town the crowd of persons journeying toward it grew greater. It was still very early, but all those with business to do had stolen a few hours from darkness in order to get it over and begin to enjoy themselves as soon as possible. Sturdy farmers, with piles of vegetables hanging from their carrying poles, trotted dully along. Men with great packages of provisions bound upon their backs went bending and grunting down the white road. There were peddlers and sweetmeat sellers, and old women with juicy stalks of sugar cane. These and a thousand more hastened toward the town.

A little man in an expensive robe ran faster than anyone. He must have been a person who owed money, for after him ran, with great determination, a tall, lean fellow in sober shopman's garb. Although it was now broad daylight, this man carried a lighted paper lantern on a bamboo stick. The people laughed to see this diverting chase. Though they had seen many like it before, such excitements never ceased to amuse. If a debt was not paid by daylight on New Year's Day, it had to be forgiven. But if the person to whom the money was owed could not catch the debtor by then, he was entitled, so long as he carried a lighted lantern, to pretend that it was still nighttime, to pursue the debtor the next morning, and catch him if he could.

The scampering debtor and the chasing creditor disappeared in the throng of people, which now pressed closely together and slowed down in order to go through the town gate. Inside, all was a roar and commotion. In street after street the shops, gaily decorated with long, trailing banners, were besieged with buyers. Everybody was shouting and laughing with the joy of the great din.

Hwang edged his way along the open shop fronts, seeking food that was both good and cheap, so as to make the most of his poor hoard of money. Passing down a small street where the firewood and charcoal sellers had their shops, he stopped suddenly outside one of them. On the wall of it was a picture of a beautiful girl. Hwang thought that he had never seen anything so perfect before.

He stood for quite a long while, scratching the back of his

head and gazing fixedly at the picture. After regarding him for some time, the shopman, a shriveled little old man, came out into the street and plucked Hwang by the arm.

"Do you wish to buy logs?" he asked, and then, having looked keenly at Hwang's poor clothes, "Or do you want work?"

"Logs?" said Hwang hesitantly, for nothing was further from his mind than firewood at that moment. "No. I was looking at that unsightly picture which no doubt you would thank me to take away from your offended eyes."

The old man took a step backward and raised both arms in dismay.

"Do you by any chance refer to this more than excellent painting here?" he asked, indicating the picture.

Hwang pretended to laugh in scorn. "I was amused at the clumsiness of the artist," he said, "but now I also see that it is in very bad condition and likely to fall apart at any moment."

The shopkeeper affected an air of jollity. He laughed and patted Hwang's shoulder in a friendly manner. "You want the picture, young man. It is yours. I ask only nine hundred coppers for it. This is a bad day for me."

"Nine hundred coppers!" said Hwang harshly. "It is not worth two hundred coppers."

"Eight hundred," snapped the shopkeeper.

"Three hundred," grunted Hwang.

"Seven hundred." The shopkeeper's mouth was tight with pleasure.

"Four hundred," said Hwang, feeling that he was being foolish.

"Six hundred." The shopkeeper made a gesture of ending his life by cutting his throat.

"Five hundred." Hwang hardly dared say so much.

The shopkeeper closed his eyes as if in pain, turned around, and walked back into his shop. Hwang did not stop him. Just before he had got inside, the shriveled man said, over his shoulder, "Very good, then. At five hundred coppers it is yours. Take it quickly, before I repent and make some savage attack upon you."

Happy at getting the picture but miserable because of his extravagance, Hwang carefully counted out the cash. With the picture rolled up in a piece of silk, he went away to continue his shopping. He had now no more than two hundred miserable coppers with which to buy food to feast himself. Never mind, he told himself, I have a fine cabbage, and with two hundred coppers I can buy two bushels of rice.

His shopping completed, Hwang hurried home to his deserted kiln. The first thing he did was to hang the picture reverently on the wall where the light through the broken door would catch it. Then he feasted soberly on plain rice and boiled cabbage, and eating this and gazing at the picture of the lovely girl, he thought he had never before celebrated so happy a New Year's Day.

On the days that followed, Hwang always, when he rose in the morning, bowed with great courtesy to the picture, just as if it were a real lady. And before he went out to work he would place what poor food he had before it and then bow again. The picture was always a comfort to his mind.

One day, about six months later, when he came home from his work, he found to his astonishment that the fire was lighted, and when he looked into the pot, there was his rice, already cooked. He thought that some kindly disposed person must have done this, so he gratefully ate his meal and placed a little of it in a bowl, as an offering to the lady in the picture. The next evening the same thing happened; and the next.

Hwang thought it was time that he found out what was really happening. So on the third evening he came early, crept very quietly up to his home, and looked in through the window hole. He saw an amazing sight. It was the lady from the picture, busying herself preparing his meal. She looked even lovelier than ever. Her hair was swept up into a shining black mound and fastened with flowers. Her lips were cherry red and her cheeks were pink blossoms. Poor Hwang stood there quite entranced. Then, turning his eyes toward the picture on the wall, he saw that it was now only a piece of white silk. He started so suddenly with surprise that a stone clattered under his foot. Knowing he was discovered, he went straight to the doorway and entered. There was nobody there. His supper was on the fire, half cooked. The picture was back upon the silk again.

Greatly excited, Hwang finished cooking his meal, and when he had eaten it, bowed profoundly to the picture and went to bed.

Next evening he was extremely cautious. More patient, making no sound, he watched adoringly through the window hole as the lady from the picture cooked his meal. Then, very carefully, on tiptoe, he stole toward the doorway. The lady's back was turned as she bent over her task. With a rush, Hwang went into the room, seized the empty picture from the wall, and quickly rolled it up.

When the lady saw what Hwang had done, she smiled and said very sweetly, "Well, in this case, I had better stay and be your wife. Then you will not be lonely any more."

Hwang was delighted at this suggestion. So they were married, and happiness far beyond the ordinary dwelt in the ruined kiln with them. Hwang thought that no man had ever before had a wife so tender and diligent and pleasing. And perhaps he was right.

At least there is no doubt that his wife brought prosperity with her, for she managed their affairs so well that their money grew as quickly as if it had roots. In a very short time they were able to pull down the old kiln and to build a splendid house in its place.

People who passed by were quite mystified. "Was this not where the old kiln used to be?" they would ask. "And yet here, in no time at all, is a grand residence."

Naturally Hwang asked his wife who she was. Many, many

times she cleverly avoided giving him an answer. At last, when he pressed her very hard, she told him. "I am the dark maiden from the Ninth Heaven," she confessed. "As a punishment for some fault of mine, I am condemned to come down onto earth for some years."

"How many years?" asked Hwang.

She would not tell him. Perhaps she could not.

After three years a pretty daughter was born, and their happiness was greater than ever. Hwang was now a man of very prosperous ways, and his whole joy was in his wife and daughter. This child, as she grew, became more and more like her mother, until when she was eight years old, it was as if a tiny lady of the picture ran laughing about the house.

One morning, the lady asked Hwang if he still kept the old roll of silk upon which her picture had once been. When Hwang said that he still had it, his wife begged him to let her see it. It is sure that Hwang would not have granted this request but for the fact that his wife was then much troubled in spirit, and seeming to have some sickness, was resting in bed. Hoping to revive her spirits, Hwang brought the plain roll of silk to her.

The lady, lying there with troubled eyes, slowly unfastened the roll and gazed at the plain white silk. And as she looked she vanished. There was no longer a lady upon the bed. There was only, lying there, a picture of a lovely lady painted upon old silk.

A Springtime Dream

O N a fresh spring morning Lee-nyiang, a magistrate's daughter, sat in a small room in the great house, taking her lessons. Her maid, a plump, laughing young person, sat with her to share her studies and to encourage her by good example.

The old tutor, with a grave face, recited a passage of high moral worth, and his two pupils were expected to repeat it after him, not once, but many times over, until it was learned by heart.

But through the open lattice the primrose sunshine of spring poured in, and from the garden came the excited chatter of birds. Somehow the liveliness of the morning infected the two maidens so that they behaved in a most unseemly fashion. Not only did Lee-nyiang pretend to forget her words, but she also invented wrong ones, so that the tutor's little wisp of gray beard twitched with annoyance.

In this naughtiness Lee-nyiang was encouraged by her mischievous little maid, until finally the lesson turned into peals of helpless laughter, and the tutor, throwing up his hands in disgust, shook his old head sorrowfully and announced that lessons were over for the day.

Thus dismissed, the two girls put their heads together to decide what to do next. The lighthearted maid suggested that they play in the garden. Lee-nyiang's honey-brown face sobered at this suggestion. It was forbidden for young female persons to appear in the garden where the gaze of ordinary passers-by might fall on them.

But it was such a thrilling morning. The scents and sounds of spring were an invitation to escape from every-day life. After a moment's hesitation, Lee-nyiang nodded her head in laughing agreement, and hand in hand the two ran out into the colored sunshine.

They did not, of course, indulge in unseemly frolics. They walked demurely around the beds of flowers, Lee-nyiang holding her gown to show the beauty of the flower-embroidered silk. They picked bold, red blossoms and adorned their hair with them, and then leaned over the little bridge of green stone to admire their reflections in the still water.

Finally, made drowsy by the fresh air, Lee-nyiang lay down on a little mound of grass. Her answers to her maid's lively conversation soon became shorter and shorter; before very long she was fast asleep. At this the little maid stole away and left her in peace.

In the sunshine which poured through the small willow tree above her, freckling her face, Lee-nyiang slept and dreamed. In her dream a young man of very attractive and worthy appearance approached her. In his hand he carried a small branch of willow. He wanted her to be his wife.

Very gladly, in her dream, Lee-nyiang agreed to this proposal; so gladly indeed that when at last she awoke she was distressed beyond measure to discover that this praiseworthy young man was only a dream. She rose, sadly, from the grassy mound and went listlessly toward the house through a garden where the flowers seemed without color and no birds sang any more.

I do not make much of little in telling this, for so heartbroken was this unhappy girl that she became sick and died.

It had been her wish that she should be buried under the little grassy hill over which the young willow waved its pale leaves, and this was faithfully done. A picture of her, young and fresh and beautiful as she had been, was set up nearby.

Two more springs came and garlanded that garden with flowers, and then a third. And on a morning of the third spring

a young scholar of good family and of exceptional handsomeness came to the garden by mistake, seeking some other family. His name was Liu. Looking around (as even well-bred persons will) before leaving, he saw the portrait which still stood by the mound. The pretty face reminded him strongly of a face he had dreamed of one spring day some years before.

If I tell how he stole the portrait and took it home with him, it is only to show how strong was his emotion, which could thus triumph over his sense of right-and-wrong behavior.

Take it home he did, and he placed it by his bed. And when he slept he dreamed. The girl he had met in his dream of a few years ago came to him and begged him to dig up her grave under the willow tree. Because he had found her, she told him, she was permitted to live again.

Liu (his name meant "willow") rose early and went to the Temple to discuss this matter; then, with a priest, he went to the garden and dug up the grave. From the ground, a beautiful maiden welcomed him with a blushing smile.

Because Lee-nyiang's father was a magistrate, he was not only astonished to be confronted with his daughter alive again, but also inclined to be upset by this sudden and irregular approach of a young man with offers of marriage. But you can be sure that he was so delighted with this happy end to the story that he gave his consent to the wedding after saying "Hum! Hum!" only a very few times.

Money Makes Cares

THERE is very good magic in this story, for it teaches something about great wealth that you ought to know before you yourself receive great wealth. Afterward is too late; knowing the story will not help you then.

Chinese history is so long that Chen Po-Shih might well be said to have been living only the other day, because it is merely a hundred years ago since he flourished as a merchant in Ch'uan-chou.

He was immensely rich, a good man, and a wise one.

What a busy life he had! Up earlier than anyone else in the morning, his day passed in a rush of business matters. A lot of money means a great deal of work in the taking care of it. All day he was interviewing people about investments, about loans, about debts, about buying and selling, and of course about taxes. Nor did evening bring him any rest. His work went on, so that he always had his dinner late, or not at all. And when bedtime came, sleep very often had to wait until he had cleared up some difficult matter in his mind.

His wife, who loved him, used to beg him to rest and enjoy himself. "Why don't you stop for awhile, and let business look after itself?" she would ask anxiously, stroking his hot forehead with long, cool fingers. But of what use were such questions? One might as well ask the man who rides the tiger, "Why don't you get off that beast's back for awhile?" He would be likely to answer, "But if I get off, this tiger will eat me." So it was, no doubt, with Chen Po-Shih and his wealth.

In the next house lived a man who was as poor as Chen was rich. Li was his name. He was no more than a laborer who worked in the fields, on the roads, anywhere there was hard work to be done. His earnings were very small. There was only just enough money to keep Li and his wife in the plainest manner of living.

All day he would toil and sweat. At evening he would come back, tired and thankful, to his small home. The first thing he always did was to give his wife all the money he had earned that day. He had nothing to worry about at all. There was a simple meal to be eaten, and then the soft evening hours were his own.

He would sit outside when it was warm, and sing, and play upon his flute, and think how lucky he was to be in such a fortunate position.

On the quiet evening air the sounds of his singing and of the pure strains of his flute would wander in through the windows of the house of Chen Po-Shih. He, to be sure, never heard them. He was much too busy. But they used to disturb the mind of Chen's good wife. How unfair it is that poor Li, with all his poverty, should be so happy, while my husband, so rich and so much wiser, must spend his days and nights with care upon his brow. Oh! How much I would like to hear my husband sing and play upon the lute!, thought Mrs. Chen.

One evening she said these thoughts to Chen Po-Shih. He stopped for a moment, and put down the abacus on which he had been adding large sums. He smiled, pleased at his wife's concern for him. "It is said of old," he reminded her, "that the poor have plenty of time. If you wish Li to stop playing and singing in the evening, I can quickly arrange that for you. But it would be a pity, I think."

"What will you do?" asked Mrs. Chen.

"I will give him some money."

Mrs. Chen laughed. It was nice to hear laughter in that great house. "But that would simply make him happier than ever," she protested.

"Let us see," said Chen. "If you hear him singing and playing tomorrow evening, you will know that I am wrong."

Early next morning, so that he would not forget, Chen sent a servant to ask Li if he would come and speak with him. Naturally Li did not disobey such a summons. As quickly as he could, he presented himself before the important man.

Chen courteously rose from his chair when Li came in. "Well, Neighbor Li," he said. "I do not meet you as often as I would wish. How is life with you? Good or bad?"

Li shuffled awkwardly on his feet. "You know how it is with laboring men like me," he said. "Always the work is too hard and the pay is too little. But, taking the ill with the good (and I've got a hard-working, sensible wife, as you know), things might be a lot worse. Indeed, we get along very happily, when I come to think of it."

Chen smiled sadly. "I have been thinking about you, Neighbor Li," he said. "I'm sure that as a laborer you don't do as well as you ought to. Now we have been neighbors for a long time and never has any unpleasantness passed between us. I would like to give you a present. Look, here are five hundred silver pieces. Take them and set up some fine, profitable business in which you and your good wife can prosper."

Li bowed almost to the ground, and did not know what to say, so profound was his gratitude. But at last he got out of the room in some manner, and ran as fast as he could to carry the news and the silver to his wife. Chen, watching his eager going, did not look at all happy.

Li did not go to work that day. He sat discussing with his wife the best way to employ this money. If they discussed one plan they must have discussed twenty, but which of these was the best, the could not decide. They talked with such earnestness that dinner was an hour late; even then, Li did not seem hungry, and hardly knew what he was eating, because his thoughts were still going around and around in his head.

Over at the great house Mrs. Chen listened long at an open window. There was no lilt of lute, no harsh, happy voice singing. She went to her husband and laid her hand on his sleeve. "You were right," she told him.

"I was afraid so," said Chen.

Even when Li went to bed he could not sleep. All night he sighed and tossed his limbs about. In the morning he crept out of bed, heavy-eyed, and went to the hiding place to make sure that the money was still safe.

For two more nights and three more days Li and his wife worried about how to use this money. Then—fortunately, I am sure—on the third night, the God of Luck appeared to Li as he lay hot and restless. "Money makes cares," said the God of Luck. "If you understand that, you need not worry about the money any more."

At once it was all clear in Li's mind; he sank into a refreshing sleep.

Early in the morning he called upon Chen.

"Ah!" said Chen. "Welcome, Neighbor Li. And have you decided on your plan yet?"

"Indeed I have," said Li cheerfully. "I have come to give back these five hundred silver pieces." And he placed the money before Chen, just as he had received it. "And I want to thank you for your kindness," he remembered to say, before hurrying away to go back to his work.

Li worked with great happiness and content that day, and in the evening the music of his lute and the warm sound of his voice again stole across the garden.

When Mrs. Chen heard it, she could not help shedding a tear. She looked across at her husband, who was, as always, busy with his figures. But he smiled back at her to show that he, too, had heard the music. And he smiled as if he were glad.

The Faithful Wife

THE Meng family and the Chiang family lived next to one another. A handsome wall of clay, surmounted by elegant blue tiles, separated their two gardens.

In springtime, as it happened, both families planted pumpkin plants, one on each side of this wall. The seasons of Little Rains and then of Great Rains came and went, and both pumpkin plants flourished excessively. By the time the great heat lay upon the country, both had climbed to the top of the wall, and there they grew together into one, and produced a solitary pumpkin. But it was such a fine one and of a size so prodigious that both families were extremely proud of it and never thought to quarrel about whose it was.

The day came when it was ripe and should be cut. By this time it had been agreed that it should be equally divided between the two families. So while Father Meng cut the pumpkin loose from the stem, all the Chiangs looked on with pride and admiration. And then, when it had been handed to Father Chiang, and he began to slice it in half, all the Mengs looked on with wonder and satisfaction.

Just as the knife was slicing through the pumpkin everyone heard a child's voice cry out: "Please be careful." Old Chiang was so startled that he dropped the pumpkin. It split open as it hit the ground, and out of it struggled a pretty little girl. All the Chiangs lifted their hands and exclaimed with delight at her beauty. All the Mengs, too, exclaimed at her beauty, but did not lift their hands, which they were using to clutch the top of the wall as they struggled to peer over at this amazing sight.

At once it was decided that both families should look after

this little fairy one, and to show that this was so, they called the child Meng Chiang.

These happy things went on during the wicked reign of the Emperor Ch'in Shih Huang-ti. There can have been few rulers as cruel as he. Yet it was he who began to build what is still one of the Seven Wonders of the World—the Great Wall of China. The Huns were at that time destroying and killing in the far north, and the Emperor sought in his mind for some way of keeping them out of China. He decided to build a wall right across the north of China, from the mountains in the west to the sea in the east.

And it was begun. But whether the plans were wrong or the builders were careless, who can tell? The fact was that almost as soon as a length of wall was built, it fell down again. The Emperor imprisoned and beheaded people, but all in vain.

A man came to him and said, "There is but one way to build the wall so that it will stand firm forever. In every mile of wall you must bury a man. Then each mile of wall will have its guard." Now ten thousand miles of wall meant ten thousand men, all to be killed, but this meant nothing to the vile Emperor. Had it been one hundred thousand men he would not have been the least bit put out. So he gave orders at once that the thousand men should be collected for this dread purpose, and the cries and lamentation of the people went up from every city, town and village.

Then a minister who was clever, and perhaps a little kind, went to the Emperor with another suggestion. "I have heard," he said, "that there is in a certain place a man named Wan. Now Wan means Ten Thousand. So if you have him, you have ten thousand."

The Emperor was highly pleased with this idea not because it saved the lives of so many innocent men but because it was so much easier and quicker to fetch just one man. He gave orders to seize him.

But Wan learned of his danger, and fled. He fled fast and he fled far—far from his own province—and he did not stop in his flight until he reached the homes of the Meng and the Chiang families. Nor would he have stopped then had he not seen the beautiful Meng Chiang, who by this time had grown into a young woman.

At once they fell in love with each other, and it was not long before they were married.

After the wedding both families sat down to a feast with the bridegroom, while the bride, as was proper, sat apart in another room, waiting till the guests, after they had eaten, should come to her and make merry. But even while Wan lifted the wine cup to drink, the Emperor's soldiers burst in and seized him. In vain did the two families wail: in vain did the beautiful wife throw herself at the soldiers' feet. Wan was carried away to be killed, to make the wall stand firm.

The lovely Meng Chiang could not be comforted. After many days she left the Meng and the Chiang families and traveled many hundreds of weary miles to search for the bones of her lost husband. Alas! When she reached the great wall, it stretched mile after mile, up and down hill and away, as far as eye could see. How could she know where in all that length of wall her husband had been buried?

It came to the ears of the Emperor that a beautiful young wife was searching up and down the wall for her husband's bones. The Emperor thought he would like to see her, and had her brought before him. When he saw her, the Emperor could think of only one thing. She was so beautiful that she must be his Empress.

When Meng Chiang heard of this, she was dreadfully angry. But the Emperor's wishes could not be denied. Meng Chiang therefore agreed to become Empress, if the Emperor would grant her three wishes. First, a festival in honor of her husband must be held. It must be a great festival, lasting forty-nine days. Then her husband must be buried honorably, and the Emperor and all the highest officials must be in attendance. And last, on the banks of the great river a terrace must be built. On the terrace she would make a sacrifice to her husband. The Emperor willingly agreed to these three conditions.

So the memory of Wan was honored by a great festival lasting forty-nine days. Then his body was reverently taken from out of the wall and buried with decent ceremony.

And when all these things were done, Meng Chiang went onto the terrace, which was now built, and in a proud voice began to curse the Emperor for his wickedness. When she had finished cursing, she cast herself into the deep river.

The Emperor was so enraged that he ordered his soldiers to cut her dead body into little pieces, but when they had done so, the pieces turned into the little silver fishes that you always see just near to the river's edge. And people say that Meng Chiang lives forever in these little silver fishes.

Chin and Yi

THEY were great friends, Chin and Yi. They were only happy when they were in each other's company. They became blood brothers. There were no two men more attached to one another in the whole of China.

Alas! Chin died. Yi would not be consoled. He had to be dragged away from his friend's grave by four strong fellows, and they afterward complained so bitterly of the hard work which this had been that each of them had to be paid five coppers extra.

Poor Yi felt that he would never be happy again. But he need not have sorrowed so heavily, for the tale of his woe reached the Underworld. It must have, because one night Chin came back to him in a dream.

Chin was richly clothed and was quick to explain to Yi that he had been made an official in the Underworld. This gave him a certain freedom of movement and an influence which he was happy to exert in favor of his friend Yi. In short, their happy friendship was by no means over, because Yi could meet Chin every day in the Underworld, if he wished. All that was needed was that Yi should retire, as if to rest. Then if he repeated the magic words which Chin now told him, he would find himself transported to the Underworld, where Chin would be waiting for him. Their old friendship could be continued in a place where the surroundings were agreeable and where refreshments were free.

When Yi awoke from this dream, he felt a great pleasure in his heart, which made him certain that his dream had been a true one. That very afternoon he lay down on his bed, and with his eyes tightly closed, repeated the magic words. He felt a surge of movement. He heard a great sighing of wind. And there he was, in the Underworld, with Chin running happily toward him, arms outstretched.

Once Yi had found this way to reach his friend, never a day passed when they were not together. Many a fine talk they had, as of old, while they sipped amber tea together. Many a bold song they sang as the hot rice wine was poured into emptied cups. Every day Yi would retire to his bed, in order to go and visit Chin.

Yi took great joy in his grandson, a little fellow of perhaps five years old, and going about Yi's house, the two were often together. One afternoon his grandson went to rest with Yi, and heard the magic words as Yi pronounced them. As soon as Yi had disappeared, the grandson—eager to copy his elders, as little children are—repeated the magic words himself. The result was that when Yi reached the Underworld, he found that he had his little grandson with him. It didn't matter one bit. There were plenty of other little boys running about there very happily. So, with the grandson pattering along behind them, the two friends strolled off for a pleasant talk.

The walk was so pleasant that Yi soon forgot all about his grandson. The child wandered off and then joined a crowd of merry children who were jumping to reach pigs' heads which were hanging on a wall. They were putting them on and laughing and playing.

When it was time to go, Yi had long forgotten all about the little boy. When he got back to the upper world, there was his grandson, lying pale and still, where he had left him on the bed. Then Yi remembered. Anxiously he called to the boy, but he could not get an answer. The child lay like one dead.

You can imagine what a fuss was made by the women of the house. Poor Yi was blamed for the lad's death.

There was nothing that Yi could say, and nothing that he

could do until he could see Chin again on the next afternoon. Never did twenty-four hours pass so slowly.

Then at last Yi was in his friend's presence again, stuttering in his anxiety to get news of his grandson.

"Most regrettable," said Chin, in a shocked voice, when Yi had told him of the loss of the boy.

"Tell me at once, where can he be?" urged Yi, clutching pitifully at Chin's arms.

Chin rubbed his cheek hard with one hand. He seemed very put out. "Who can say?" he said sadly.

"Who can say?" almost shrieked Yi. "This is dreadful. He cannot just disappear."

"Oh! But he can," Chin told him, almost blandly, for he had now been an official for quite a long time. "However, I will consult the Lists of the Living and the Dead. Perhaps in them we shall find some mention of your grandson."

This took quite a long time, during which Yi, in dreadful anxiety, stood first on one foot and then on the other. Moreover, he was continually interfering with Chin, who was busily unrolling and studying scroll after scroll of names and particulars.

"Please do not interrupt," Chin had to tell him, again and again.

At last Chin rapped a scroll triumphantly with his forefinger. "This is it," he announced, with a happy smile. "The boy has been reborn as a pig in the house of the Han family in Hsing-hua fu. How fortunate!"

"Fortunate?" shouted Yi in a bitter voice. "A few more pieces of luck like that, and my whole family will be dead and forgotten." He laughed an unhappy laugh. "Pray tell me, what is there so fortunate in being reborn a pig?"

Chin was aware that he had not, in his zeal as an official, been quite helpful enough. He hastened to reassure Yi. "The good fortune, dear friend, lies in the fact that the village of Hsing-hua fu is so close to your own. You will not, therefore, have to exert yourself to any great extent to recover your grandson."

Hearing this, Yi was vastly relieved in mind. What must he do? he asked.

"Go quickly to the house of Han in the village of Hsing-hua fu," advised Chin. "There you will find a sow with thirteen newborn piglets. But the one with the white star on its fore-head. When you have killed this one, you will have your grand-son back alive!"

Yi hurried back to earth as quickly as he could. He called at his own house, to provide himself with money and to warn those who were there not on any account to bury his grand-son's body. Then with all haste he sped to Hsing-hua fu. There at the house of the Han family he found that a sow had just had thirteen piglets. He bought the one with a white star on its forehead. He did not bargain over the price. This surprised the farmer, who was even more surprised when Yi killed the piglet on the spot and then ran away with frantic haste.

Yi ran all the way home. At the doorway of his house, alive and well, waiting to greet him, was his little grandson.

The Brave Actor

T HERE was once an actor who was quite fearless. He did
not care for any man or for wild beasts or even for spirits.
When people who were frightened of darkness used to
keep closely indoors at night, this man used to roam about
quite freely, even when there was no moon to light his way.

One night, after the theatre had closed, he was walking very
happily along a road outside the city. A thin mist from off the
rice fields on either side of him was swirling across his path.
Suddenly, coming toward him, he saw a young woman. It was so
remarkable to meet a young woman alone at night, that the
actor stopped her and asked her gaily who she was.

She did not answer him, but stood still and turned her face
away.

He asked her again who she was.

"I am a ghost," the girl answered.

"How exciting!" exclaimed the actor. "Now, I have always
wanted to meet a ghost. Please don't go away. Is it true that
ghosts turn themselves into all sorts of things? I do hope it is!"

"Yes, it is quite true," the young woman answered in a soft
voice.

"Please do show me something, then?" pleaded the actor.
"Do let me see what you can do?"

The ghost throught she would teach this bold young man a
lesson, so she turned herself into a hideous old man whose long,
dirty hair hung right down to the ground.

The actor laughed heartily and applauded this feat. "Not at
all bad," he said. "But the long pheasant feathers we wear on

165

the stage, when we are dressed as great military commanders, are just as imposing as that."

Rather angrily, the ghost turned into a girl again.

"I'm sure you can do better than that," said the actor.

So the ghost turned into an old woman with a fearful cut across her face.

The actor was quite scornful. "On the stage, with a bit of red paint, we can make ourselves look worse than that," he told her.

The ghost (it was by now a girl again) hurriedly turned into a nasty-looking robber with great, long teeth.

The actor simply laughed. "You are getting worse, not better," he said. "If you can't do something more than that, I'm afraid I shall not think much of you. Now do try hard. Do something really scaring."

But the poor ghost once more turned into a girl, who, hanging her head, admitted that she could do no better than that.

"Well," said the actor cheerfully, "let me have a turn. And he took his trumpet and pulled it out till it was twice as long. Then he pulled it out again, longer still. A third time he pulled it, and it was then as long as a man. "Now stay here," he begged. "After I have blown my trumpet, then I will show you some of my tricks." And he blew such a blast on the trumpet that the mist fled away. But the ghost was so frightened by this dread noise that she ran away, too, as fast as she could.

The actor was sadly disappointed by this, as he had hoped for quite a jolly evening, but when he saw that there was no hope of the ghost returning, he went home himself.

Now it happened that for quite awhile he did not go out again at night to wander in the darkness. But the first time he did so he met the same ghost again. This time, behind her, was a large number of other ghosts. And this time it was the ghost who spoke first.

"Aha!" she said. "I have been seeking you ever since our last meeting. I have very much wanted to find out which of us is the stronger."

Then she gave a signal to the other ghosts, who all sprang upon the actor and began to beat him.

The actor started to shout and howl, but when that seemed only to encourage the ghosts to beat him harder, he thought he might as well take a hand in this fight himself. So he laid about him as heartily as he could, and rained blows at every ghost he could reach. Indeed, so quickly did he deliver his blows and so careless was he of who and where he was hitting, that he gave the ground a hearty buffet two or three times.

It happened that on the spot where this flight was taking place there was an old grave, and it was not more than a few moments before an old man popped out of the grave, to ask who was knocking there.

The ghosts, seeing this new ghost, did not like to offend him further, and ran away as far as they could. The actor, glad of any interruption to his beating, at once asked the old man to protect him.

In this the actor was very lucky. In China it is the greatest of misfortunes for a man to die without leaving any sons, because if there are no sons there is no one to make offerings at the grave at the Clear Bright Festival in the spring; as a result, the journey of the dead toward Paradise is made much slower and more tedious.

This ghost said, "Certainly I will protect you. I have left no sons behind me on earth. If you will do the services to me that a son would have done, I will protect you now and I will help you all your life."

And it is good to say that each of them kept their word. The actor prospered and enjoyed long life and good fortune, and on every feast day he always remembered to bring sacrifices to the grave of the lonely old man.

The Two Brothers

THERE was once a man who was rich enough to have nearly everything that he desired. He had a fine house, a great stretch of farmland, many servants, a beautiful wife, and two sons. Nobody wanted for anything in that household.

But in course of time his wife died, and then the rich man himself was gathered to his fathers. It was left to his two sons to share the land and all the possessions.

The elder son was tall and lean and greedy. The younger one was short and plump and of such a merry mind that he did not give much thought to business affairs. As a result, when the sharing out was done, the elder son had everything that was of any value. All that was left for the younger son was a small piece of stony ground that was not fit for growing anything.

It is not surprising, then, that as the years went by the grasping elder brother grew even richer than his father had been. But the younger brother, with his carefree nature and his unprofitable field, began to find it more and more difficult to live at all.

At first he was able to borrow small sums of money by pawning his little plot of land, but when these sums were spent and when no one would lend him more, he was in a pitiable state. His cheerful plumpness diminished until his cheeks hung loosely upon his face, and his beautiful round stomach, which had been such a source of pride to him, flapped empty. There were many days when he did not eat at all.

In this plight he sought out his elder brother and begged him, out of his plenty, to spare a little for his famished younger brother. But (as does happen sometimes) the result of prosper-

ing had been to make the elder brother meaner and more grasping than ever before. He would not give his younger brother
even so much as a grain of rice.

At this cruel disappointment, the cheerfulness with which the
younger brother had borne his troubles at last broke down. On
a boulder, by the side of the lane, a little way from his brother's
fine house, he sat down and wept.

Not often do the sobs of honest and cheerful men escape the
ears of the Jade Emperor of Heaven. So it was not likely that
this weeping would be unheard. For, truth to tell, when the
younger brother did at last break down and weep in this manner, I am sure that he wept longer and louder than any wronged
man has wept before or since. He wept for the vile conduct of
his older brother; he wept for the vanished delights of rich
food and soft clothes; he wept for the plump face that he had
lost and for his once beautiful, round stomach.

Such a weeping affected the Jade Emperor of Heaven very
profoundly. He summoned one of his ministers. "There seems to
be a man weeping with remarkable violence down there on
earth," he said. "Go quickly and discover what moves him.
I fear some enormous wrong has been done."

The minister, who was a very important personage in the
Heavens, was at that time busy with many great affairs. Very
tactfully, he suggested, "Would it not be more in order if we
called for a report first from one of the local gods?" The Jade
Emperor thought this a sound suggestion, and a message was
sent at once to one of the local gods to come and make a report
on this matter to the Court of Heaven.

A local god accordingly leapt upon a cloud which happened
to be passing, and appeared humbly before the Emperor, to
whom he explained all the facts in this painful case.

The Jade Emperor of Heaven was much moved by the story.
"Surely this good man suffer's great wrong," he said. "Now,
what shall I do to help him?" His face lit up with the joy of
doing good. "I think I will send him the narcissus flower. By

growing this and selling the bulbs, the younger brother can make good profit."

The minister objected. "But surely," he said, "everybody else, seeing the beauty of this flower, will copy it. And where then will be the younger brother's profit?"

"Ah!" said the Emperor. "But the narcissus grows only on such stony and sandy ground as the younger brother has."

"True," answered the minister. "But many people also have such stony and sandy ground."

The Emperor of Heaven was put out for a moment. Then he clapped his hands and said, laughing, "Now I see what to do. I will work some magic upon this narcissus. Then when it is transplanted from the younger brother's land, it will flower only once and not again. In this way people will be forced to come back to the younger brother every year to buy more. Is this not a good plan?"

"It is a wise and memorable plan!" exclaimed the minister, who had been a minister for a long time and knew just what to say.

"Magnificent," said the local god, so that his presence should not be overlooked.

So when they had feasted a great deal to celebrate this decision, the local god was sent down to earth to give the narcissus bulb to the younger brother.

The local god changed into the shape of an old man, and thus disguised went up to the younger brother, who was still weeping, but hoarsely now. The old man put a hand on the weeper's shoulder, and said, "Weep no more. Heaven is not deaf to the cry of the afflicted. Here from the Jade Emperor of Heaven himself is the narcissus bulb. Plant this on your little piece of land, and soon people will come crowding to buy bulbs that flower like it, and you will become rich."

The younger brother was not so easily comforted. "How shall I become rich by selling flower bulbs?" he asked. "Even if this were to grow and multiply on my thin land, customers would only buy once. After that they would grow their own, and nobody would want my flower bulbs any more."

"That has all been arranged," the local god assured him. "This flower will only grow and multiply on your own land. It will not do so anywhere else. A powerful work of magic has been done upon it."

"Can it be true that the Jade Emperor of Heaven would take so much trouble for so insignificant a person as myself?" the younger brother asked him. But the old man had disappeared.

Then the younger brother knew that he truly had been talking to a god.

You may be sure that after that the younger brother lost no time in planting the narcissus bulb in his barren land, and it flourished and spread to an extent that no one who had not actually seen this wonder could believe it. It was not long before it covered the whole ground.

By the New Year, the narcissus garden was alive with beautiful flowers, all lifting their pure heads to Heaven and jostling happily in the breeze. The rich scent attracted buyers, as much as the beautiful shape and color. People flocked to buy these bulbs until the younger brother could spare no more. He now had money in plenty.

Of course each buyer was intending to grow new plants from those he had bought, so that he would not have to buy from the younger brother any more. But, behold, as the Jade Emperor of Heaven had intended, all the plants that had been bought flowered for just one year and then never again. Meanwhile, on the younger brother's plot the narcissus plants flowered again and again, year after year.

So with all those who loved these gay flowers coming to him year after year to buy fresh bulbs of narcissus at high prices, the younger brother grew richer and richer. Very soon he could afford servants in plenty, rich clothes and sumptuous food.

And as when one bucket comes up from the well full, then the other bucket must go down empty, so while the younger brother prospered, the elder brother fell upon hard times. And the story ends with the younger brother sitting at ease in lavish surroundings, with plump cheeks and a prosperous stomach, while the elder brother, thinner than ever, has to work hard from morn till night so that he can earn just enough to eat.

The Fairy Grotto

T HERE were two boys who were cousins. One day they took wooden buckets and went to a distant spring to fetch water. The water at this spring was of especial sweetness.

When they got there, they filled their buckets and set them down by the spring's brink. It was early summer, and wild flowers clustered all around them. Little red birds with heads of blue sang *"Chip, Chip,"* and then chased each other. And brilliant butterflies, as big as a man's hand, fluttered from flower to flower.

It was all so delightful that the cousins strolled off to enjoy the summer scene. As boys will, they wandered away farther than they had intended, over hill, across valley, until, to their surprise, they came to the entrance of a cave.

On each side of the entrance was a big stone, and on each stone sat a fairy. These two fairies were intently playing chess.

The two boys, who had been brought up to observe the rules of good behavior, did not interrupt, but stood silent, watching the game.

Just in front of the fairies was a white hare which did not stop jumping up and down. The boys noticed an odd thing. Each time the white hare leapt, all the flowers in the grass bloomed and nodded. Each time the white hare sank to the ground, the flowers all faded and died.

At last the game of chess ended. Not till then did the fairies notice the two boys.

"How long have you been waiting here?" asked one of the fairies.

They told her that they had been standing and watching the game for about two hours.

At this both fairies looked very grave.

"And now we must go home," said the elder boy.

"Don't do that," said the fairies. "Stay here in the grotto. If you go home, nobody will recognize you."

But the boys insisted that they must go back.

The fairies seemed quite upset, but as they could not dissuade them, they gave each of the boys a piece of reed. "If you do not find home agreeable, come back," they said. "If you point at this rock with your reeds, the cavern will open for you."

Then the fairies picked up their chess pieces and went quite sadly into the cavern, and when they were in, the rock wall closed up so tightly that no entrance could be seen.

The boys scampered off and found their way back to the spring. But everything was altered. There was the spring, but instead of a field of flowers, a grove of ancient pine trees surrounded the water pool. Quite mystified, the boys made their way back to the village. But it was not there. Where seemly houses had stood, there were now mounds of weed-covered earth.

Outside a ruined hut sat two ancient men. The boys went up to them, and bowing decently, asked where their home had gone.

"Whose home? Who are you?" croaked one of the ancient men in an irritable tone.

"My name is Liu Chu'an," the elder boy said, "and this is my cousin Yuan Chao. We live here in Lung Ch'a, but our house has gone."

The other old man uttered a nasty laugh.

"Liu Chu'an!" he grunted. "Yuan Chao! Are you young rascals trying to make a mock of us?"

"You'd better not," rasped the first ancient man, and his beard wagged with anger. "Liu Chu'an and Yuan Chao were

our ancestors. We are their descendants of the seventh generation."

The boys were almost distracted. How were they to know that the white hare, which they had seen jumping up and down for two hours outside the fairy grotto, was the Fairy of the Seasons? Each jump was a spring, summer, autumn and winter. For four hundred years the boys had stood, silent, watching that game of chess and the jumping hare.

But not knowing this, they persisted in claiming to be Liu Chu'an and Yuan Chao, until the old men raised their cracked voices and summoned the few other scraggy people who were left in the village. These, cursing the boys for baiting such venerable men, gave them both a good beating and drove them away.

It was then that they remembered what the fairies had said. They made their way back to the fairy grotto, but when they got there they no longer had their reeds with them. No doubt they had dropped them in their haste to get away from the villagers.

In vain they knocked against the walls of the fairy grotto. Nobody answered them. In their grief they both died, or perhaps they had already been dead for nearly four hundred years. Nobody can say.

But the Ruler of Heaven was saddened by their unhappy fate, and to compensate them, he made Liu Chu'an the God of Good Luck, and Yuan Chao the God of Ill Fortune.

The Lucky Serving Maid

THERE once lived a rich man and his wife. They had no children and loved nobody at all. Instead of sharing a little of the good things of life with beggars who came to ask for charity, they drove them away with curses and heavy blows.

To make life easier for themselves, they bought a servant girl from a distant province. It was she who was expected to do every bit of work. It was of no use for the poor young creature to work every hour of daylight, in the hope of finishing her tasks and being permitted a little time to walk in the village and have a small rest. That was useless, because if all the work that had to be done was completed, the old wife would quickly think of something else that would keep the girl busy.

You can imagine that this poor slave often wept quietly and lamented her fate. The women of the province from which she came were not usually very good to look at; this girl, like them, had an unattractive, dark and lumpish face. It was not likely that any rich young man would like her well enough to buy her from the old couple, to be his wife. So she had a whole lifetime of hard work to look forward to, and harsh treatment as well.

Yes, there was harsh treatment in plenty, for both the man and the wife were so mean and spiteful that the poor maid was beaten with sticks for the least fault.

"By what ill-luck am I doomed to a life like this?" the maiden used to ask, lifting her unattractive face to Heaven.

These sad words at last reached the ears of the Immortals and the Gods. They were not happy to hear of such misery. One of the Eight Immortals (it was Ho-ho Tzu) put aside his feather fan and his peach of immortality, and went down to earth to see

179

what was the matter. As soon as he reached the earth he assumed the shape of a wretched beggar, and shuffling painfully along on bare feet, he reached the house of the rich couple.

Outside the gate he stretched his arms out of his dirty rag of a gown and began to shout loudly for charity. "Noble sir, honorable mother of this house! Give me something to eat. See, I die here of hunger!"

It was a good thing that he old couple were out, or Ho-ho Tzu would surely have been greeted with bitter words and sent stumbling away with heavy blows. As it was, there was only the poor serving maid at home, and she, who knew what hunger was, felt very sorry for the poor beggar.

She did not dare give him any food from the house. The old couple would have discovered such a thing as soon as they came home, for the first thing they did when they returned from an outing was to make sure that nothing had been taken. Why, I believe that if their maid had given away food, they would have been so furious that they would have beaten her to death.

As it was, the maid, at the moment when the beggar began to cry out for food, was stoking the fire with rice straw. This was what was used for fuel in that part of China. Now sometimes a few grains of rice were left on the rice stalks, and the poor girl, always hungry herself, had put these grains of rice aside, one by one, whenever she had found them. She now had nearly a thousand grains of rice hidden away.

Moved with pity at the beggar's plight, she ran quickly and took out her small bag of rice. This she offered to the hungry man. "Take this," she said, a smile of goodness brightening her heavy face. "It is all my own. But go quickly. My master is a hard man. He will beat you if he finds you here."

The beggar accepted the bag of rice very gratefully. Then he gave the servant girl an old rag of cloth. "You must always wash your face with this cloth," he said. "But take great care. Do not let anyone else use it." It was a useless-looking scrap, but the servant could see that the beggar wanted to make her some sort

of present in this way, so she thanked him very warmly, just as if it had been something valuable.

While she was doing so, the old couple came back. They both scuttled up toward the beggar and the maid, their hard faces twisted with suspicion.

"Have you given this old wretch anything of ours?" snapped the rich man, his eyes peering here and there.

"If she has, we will soon seize it back," screeched the old woman, trying to bar the beggar's way.

"This man has had nothing belonging to you," said the maid-servant quite truthfully, turning toward the beggar so that he could support her. But he had disappeared. Ho-ho Tzu had grown tired of being a beggar.

For a moment the old man and his wife looked at the spot where the beggar had been. Then they both shook their heads, and no doubt in order to take their minds off the matter, began to beat their servant.

Next morning, when she washed, the girl remembered to use the scrap of cloth that the beggar had given her. It was something of her own, and it was the first gift she had had since she had been sold to her present master. She used the cloth every morning. After awhile (there was no mistaking it) her dark face began to get whiter and whiter; at the same time it became more and more attractive to look at. She soon grew so beautiful that even her master and mistress noticed the change.

These envious people guessed that there was some secret to be discovered, and they questioned the poor girl night and day. It was only after a very heavy beating that the maid confessed that it was the old piece of cloth that had turned her ugliness into beauty.

Nothing would satisfy the old people but that they should have it, and with threats and blows they took from the maid her precious piece of rag.

Gleefully, next morning, the harsh man and his wicked wife washed their faces with the cloth. When it had made them both beautiful, they intended to hire it out to other ugly people at a high price. After they had thoroughly soaked their faces, they both ran eagerly to the mirror. When they looked in it, two monkey faces grinned back at them, and even while they stood there, stupefied, long monkey hair began to grow all over their bodies. Wild with shame and terror, they ran away into the woods, and were never seen again.

The lucky maid, left with a fine house and all their money, could look forward to a happy future. And she did not have to look far, because in no time at all, a rich young man of good character was so struck by her beauty and good temper that he made her his wife.

The Red-Maned Horse

THE most beautiful daughter of the Prime Minister, and what was just as important, the best educated, was Pao-ch'uan. She was young and lovely. It was time that her parents arranged a marriage for her.

There were many men of high position who were anxious to become her husband. But even all those many years ago a prime minister's position was a difficult one. It would have been very easy for the father of Pao-ch'uan to choose a suitable husband for her, but when he had done so, how many proud families with disappointed sons would have become his bitter enemies?

So, thinking how best to avoid such troubles, the Prime Minister hit upon a plan. In the garden he had a tower erected, elegant in shape and hung with bright flowers.

Then he summoned his youngest daughter.

She came, fluttering, in a fine robe of lightest blue. She bowed and awaited his word.

"Daughter," said the Prime Minister (for because he loved this daughter very greatly he always tried to speak with severity, in order to hide this weakness), "tomorrow you will choose a husband."

The girl's eyes opened wide in astonishment. It was not a young woman's privilege to have any say in the choice of her husband.

"But, Father, how shall I do such a bold thing?"

"It is arranged," said the Prime Minister, tapping his forehead with his fan, to show that he had been doing much thinking. "Tomorrow morning you will stand on the tower that is built in the garden. Here is a ball." And he handed her a beautiful ball embroidered in five colors. "Those who are willing to marry you will wait below in the garden. You will throw down

183

the ball. He who catches it will become your husband. In this way it will be decided." He waved his hand to dismiss her, and bowing again, Pao-ch'uan flitted away.

This was quite an important matter, thought Pao-ch'uan, and so, as she did when there was something on her mind, she went out into the garden. It was surrounded by a very high wall and was therefore a suitable place for quiet thoughts.

As she walked there she saw to her amazement a young beggar lad, asleep upon a bank of grass. Though his clothes were tattered, he had a clean and superior face. Pao-ch'uan awoke him at once.

"What are you doing in this place, beggarman?" she asked him. Her voice was like the clear tinkling of a little fall of water.

"The gate was open. I was tired. I came in," he said, and something in his confident tones told Pao-ch'uan that this young fellow was born to become a great man.

"But this is the garden of the Prime Minister. You will be executed if you are found here," urged the young lady.

It was a matter of little account, he told her. He was rested now. He would go.

But Pao-ch'uan did not want him to be gone so quickly. To keep him for a little while, she began to tell him about the arrangements for her to choose a husband next day. As she talked, the more she looked at this young man, the more she liked him. So she gave him some gold, and told him to buy fine clothing such as a young lord would wear. "And come to-morrow and try your fortune," she said shyly to him, before he went.

You may be sure that there was a great commotion in that gay garden the next morning. Scores of young men of high position jostled and struggled at the foot of the tower. And on the tower itself stood Pao-ch'uan, radiant in the bright sunshine, holding in her little hand the five-colored ball.

She tossed it into the air. There was a yell of excitement from the young lords beneath. Each one shouted to know who had caught the ball; then in a moment they were all scrambling about upon the ground, thinking that it had fallen beneath their feet. And all the time, a little apart, Sieh (for that was the beggar's name), in splendid robes, stood quietly with the five-colored ball in his hand.

"How had it got there?" asked everyone. I think that Pao-ch'uan had thrown it straight to him.

The Prime Minister lost no time in proclaiming this young man as betrothed to his daughter. But then, puzzled because he did not recognize him, he began to make enquiries. When he found that Sieh was a beggar, the Prime Minister was greatly enraged. The marriage must not take place.

But it must, urged Pao-ch'uan. Her father had given his word.

It must not, raged the father. The young man had grossly deceived them all.

She would marry him, insisted Pao-ch'uan.

If she did, she would leave home never to return. This was the Prime Minister's final word.

Pao-ch'uan would not yield. Rather than abandon Sieh, she would leave her home. She approached closely to her father. They clasped each other's hands three times, to show that the matter was agreed upon.

And away from the fine house and the rich food, away from the father and mother who loved her, went Pao-ch'uan; away with Sieh to live with him in his damp beggar's cave.

There, though they lived in great poverty, the young husband soon began to show that Pao-ch'uan's opinion of him had been correct. He always had thoughts of glory in his mind.

In that district there was a very savage wild horse of great speed. No man could tame it. It was of unusual size, and its mane was blood red in color. To the astonishment of everyone, young Sieh succeeded in catching and taming this wonderful beast. The fame of this deed and the fact that he now had a splendid horse of his own made it possible for Sieh to seek a career in the army.

It was a parting of much sadness when Sieh bade farewell to his young wife and went away to seek glory in the wars. Sieh begged Pao-ch'uan to submit to her father and return to her home. He did not know how many years it might be before he came back from the fighting. He might well lose his life in some far-off and unremembered battle.

Pao-ch'uan wept at these dreadful words, but her mind was firm. She would never return to her father's house until she could go there with her husband, and then only when he had shown that he was a man of great importance.

Hastily mounting the red-maned horse—for, truth to tell, he was himself very near to tears—Sieh galloped away.

Alas! His career in the army did not start under very favorable omens. He found that he was to serve under two redoubtable commanders, General Soo and General Wei. These men were the husbands of Pao-ch'uan's two elder sisters. They hated Sieh for having brought disgrace into the family, and their hatred had every excuse for unfriendly treatment of Sieh, because of the fact that the Prime Minister had given them orders to make quite sure that Sieh was killed.

And so not only did Sieh find himself treated with harsh disdain, but it also seemed always to happen that if some daring and desperate work were to be done, it was Sieh who was put in charge of the business. Sieh soon became quite used to escaping death by a hairsbreadth. If he were sent forward, ahead of the army, to make sure of the way, it was certain that he would be ambushed by enemy troops. If he were told to climb to the top of a crag to spy out the country, an enemy archer would surely be so placed as to be able to send an arrow through his sleeve. If he were ordered to stay behind and hasten the progress of the baggage carts, he could depend upon it that the baggage train would be cut off by marauding foes. Such excitements were quite enjoyable to the grave Sieh, but he could not help admitting to himself that his chances of long life were becoming notably less.

And indeed it was no more than two years after his departure that news came that Sieh had been slain. The wife of the Prime Minister, in her fine clothing, came with her attendants to her daughter's miserable cave. Pao-ch'uan, in wretched rags, came out and knelt in dutiful welcome to her mother. It was in the mother's mind that now that Sieh was dead her daughter would give up this dreadful defiance of her father and return to live happily at home again.

But Pao-ch'uan was too devoted to the memory of her husband. In spite of all that the wife of the Prime Minister could say, she would not go with her. Mother and daughter wept for a little while in the pale winter sunlight, outside the dripping cave. Then they parted.

But I have still a tale to tell. The report that Sieh had died was not true, although those who had made it had thought it to be. What had happened was that General Wei, despairing of getting rid of Sieh by sending him on dangerous missions, had at last hit upon a plan which he was sure would mean his death.

The general pretended to have become fond of Sieh, and he invited him to a feast in order to do honor to his many brave deeds. At this feast there was a great eating and drinking, and many fine compliments were paid to the young hero. Then, when Sieh slept soundly, General Wei had the young man bound tightly to his horse.

Across on the other side of the valley the campfires of the enemy twinkled like stars. General Wei had the red-maned horse turned toward the enemy army, with Sieh bound firmly in the saddle. With a cut of the whip, the general sent the great steed galloping down the slope, away across the valley toward those hostile campfires. And to make certain that the enemy would be on the alert to receive Sieh, General Wei ordered the great war gongs to be beaten.

As the wild horse thundered across the plain, the thousand campfires of the foe went out, one by one. And in answer to the alarm that General Wei had given, the enemy war gongs dinned until the skies echoed. General Wei did not expect to be troubled further with this young upstart.

Of course Sieh was at last captured in this way, and he was to be executed as soon as there was light enough to cut off his head. But then, in the strange manner in which things do fall out, he was saved by the warrior princess who commanded the foreign troops. She had long admired his bravery in battle, and when she sent for him, out of curiosity, she was quite overcome by his handsome appearance. She would hear of no denial. He must marry her.

You must understand that Sieh did so with some reluctance. His heart still rested with his first wife Pao-ch'uan, but on the other hand he had to choose between execution and marriage to the princess. It is hard to blame Sieh for choosing marriage.

And so Sieh became the husband of the princess, and could expect that when her father the King passed to his ancestors, he would become ruler in his stead. And he was as happy as a man can be when he has wealth and ease and the prospect of a kingdom, but is living with the wrong wife.

Meanwhile Pao-ch'uan still dwelt in her beggar cave, alone and faithful. She could not believe that her high-spirited husband was really dead. Each springtime she watched for the return of the sweet birds who spent their winters in those far lands where the war still went on. Perhaps loneliness and longing were affecting her mind, because she fell into the habit of talking to these fluttering spring visitors. She used to ask if any one of them had seen her fine husband in those distant lands. Perhaps one of them would take a message to him, she used to suggest.

One spring morning (it was the eighteenth spring since Sieh had gone away) when she was talking wildly in this fashion, one of the little yellow-blue birds seemed to nod its head, as if agreeing to her request. Laughing with foolish delight, Pao-ch'uan held out her hand. The bird swooped down and alighted upon her wrist, looking up into her face with bright, encouraging eyes. Then with one stroke of its wings, it flew up onto her shoulder and rubbed its soft head against her neck.

Trembling with excitement, Pao-ch'uan tore off a piece of her tattered gown, and gashing her finger on a sharp stone, wrote a message to Sieh in her own blood on the stained fragment of cotton. The message begged Sieh to return to Pao-ch'uan before she should die of heartbreak.

This done, the lady tied the message tenderly to the bird's leg, and lifting this frail messenger upon her finger, tossed it into the sparkling air. There was a flash of blue and yellow against the pale blue sky, and then the bird's shape diminished rapidly with distance until Pao-ch'uan could see only a tiny, dark speck speeding away toward where, hundreds of miles across the plain, two armies still wrestled in war.

Straight to Sieh in the foreign kingdom the little bird flew. Sieh was no longer a young man, but a general of high renown and the chief counselor of his father-in-law, the old King. Sieh had just left a meeting of the council and was resting upon a balcony of the palace and enjoying the sight of spring blossoms in the gardens below, when he noticed the little bird. He could scarcely fail to do so, for its gay feathers draggled with travel, it continually fluttered up against him, as if trying to attract his attention. Presently Sieh noticed the piece of cloth tied to the bird's leg. He took it off. On it was written the message from his first-loved wife.

Sieh's heart gave a great leap of anxiety, and at once he ran to the royal stables, and when his red-maned horse had been led out, he leapt upon its back and thundered away. Across plain and mountain and river, the rider and horse hastened without pause. But the red-maned horse was aged now. Just at the frontier Sieh's princess wife, who, with her attendants, had followed upon the swiftest steeds in the royal stables, overtook him.

The face of the warrior princess was terrible with anger when she confronted her fleeing husband. Sieh told her the entire story, and took from his breast the tattered cotton message to show her. The princess was very much affected by this sad situation, and bade Sieh go straight to his first wife and to do then what seemed best to him.

So they parted, those two. The princess went sorrowfully back to the palace, and Sieh turned his horse's head again toward his old home. Shaking his red mane bravely, the old horse cantered on over the countless miles.

It was now the season of Great Heat, and Pao-ch'uan was sitting outside her cave in the still of evening, making baskets of bamboo to sell. In the quietness she heard on the ground the thud of great hoofs. Her hands stopped their busy plaiting. She did not stir. Across her sorrow-pale cheeks a flush of joy slowly spread. The hoof beats drew nearer, and presently, into the clearing where she sat, bounded a great horse with a red mane. The horse was drawn up in front of Pao-ch'uan and, scarcely daring to hope, she lifted her eyes.

She recognized instantly the red-maned horse, but could this man be her young husband Sieh? This was a grave, grand personage. The heavy embroidered robe and the rich coat over it showed that here was a man of great importance. Could it be Sieh? Pao-ch'uan gave a great cry of happiness. There was no doubt of it. The eyes that looked down at her with such longing were her own, dear husband's eyes.

In a moment Sieh was off his horse and was devoting himself to comforting his first-loved wife. If the blue-yellow bird had been there to see, I think his little heart would have burst for joy.

Did Pao-ch'uan reproach Sieh for his eighteen-year-old absence? You may be sure she did not. But it can be assumed that Sieh reproached himself, for he did ask earnestly for his wife's forgiveness, and he went down upon his knees to do so. In this way of showing how sorry he was, he could not have done much more. In China there is an ancient saying: "There is gold under a man's knees. He cannot bend them to a woman."